Modern Bodybuil‹

C000276612

The Natural Way to
Health and Strength

MODERN BODYBUILDING

THE NATURAL WAY TO HEALTH AND STRENGTH

Eddie Ferrie & Dennis Oakes

The Crowood Press

First published in 1997 by
The Crowood Press Ltd
Ramsbury, Marlborough
Wiltshire SN8 2HR

British Library Cataloguing-in-Publication Data
A catalogue record for this book is available from the British Library.

ISBN 1 86126 087 3

Line drawings by Annette Findlay.

Photograph previous page: J. D. Dawadu, top-level bodybuilding competitor at International level professional muscularity.

Dedication

To our parents Eddie and Elsie and Dennis and Ruby, and for Eva Garcés and for Reiss: when memories are faithful, no distance can divide.

Acknowledgements

A number of people helped us in the production of this book and we would like to thank the following:
Juan Manuel Naranjo Lopez Cepero for being a great training partner and for demonstrating some of the exercises and arranging and assisting with the photographic sessions at Chapin Sports Complex and Zeus gym; Ausunción Ciria Peñaluer for assisting in demonstrating the stretching exercises; Manuel Macías Nieto owner of Zeus for letting us take photographs there; Maria Revelles for feedback, enthusiasm, support and inspiration and for being a superb training partner.

Denny would also like to thank the following people for the help and support they gave him throughout his bodybuilding life: Andre Croft, Lawrence McFoy, Ron Francis, Trevor Green, Sean Clark, Sean O'Reilly, Wag and Diane Benett, Brian Buchanan, Wilf Sylvester, J. D. Dawadu, Jamo Nezzar, Angelito di Lester, Mickey Dunn, Lee Peskett, Ray and John from World Gym and Eduardo Merini Postigo.

Special thanks to Roger Shelley for permission to use his excellent pre-contest shots of Denny on pages 168–71, 180, 182 and 188. Roger can be contacted on 061 860 5262

Eddie would especially like to thank his wife Salud for her patience and support and finally Mr Duffy who as a young teacher taught him how to make his first Interest Book, which undoubtedly made all the difference.

Typeface used: Galliard.

Edited and designed by
D & N Publishing
Membury Business Park, Lambourn Woodlands
Hungerford, Berkshire.

Printed and bound by WBC Book Manufacturers Ltd, Mid Glamorgan.

Contents

1 History and Development of Bodybuilding

INTRODUCTION

The recent rapid growth in the popularity of bodybuilding is a remarkable cultural phenomenon. From being a form of subculture associated initially (and mistakenly) with black prison inmates in the USA, or homosexuals it has grown into an activity enjoyed worldwide by millions of people from all walks of life. One of the two principal contributing factors to the rapid and massive popularization of bodybuilding, which began to take place in the 1970s and 1980s and has continued through to the present day, was the marketing genius of American publisher Joe Weider. *Muscle and Fitness*, his top selling magazine is often described as 'the bible of bodybuilding as a lifestyle' and has a world readership of over 8,000,000. The other contributing factor was the emergence of the phenomenally successful bodybuilding champion and actor, the Austrian- born Arnold Schwarzenegger, who almost single handedly transformed bodybuilding into something with a much broader social appeal and acceptability.

To the uninitiated, the popularity of bodybuilding may be difficult to grasp. In Great Britain, the bodybuilding press has always been a little-known or understood subculture. Magazines with low circulations written for and by enthusiasts, such as *Iron Man, Body Power, Strength Athlete* and the like, provided people with information about training and competitions, but never achieved the kind of circulation enjoyed by *Muscle and Fitness* magazine. Bodybuilding was seen very much as a health-and-strength cult – in most people's eyes it probably had something to do with naturism.

Bodybuilding's appeal has been the subject of considerable study however. It has been linked to certain genetically predetermined physical, sexual and biological drives, and descriptions and explanations have come from the disparate fields of psychology, sociology and anthropology. People also often get confused by the distinction between 'bodybuilding', 'Olympic weightlifting', 'weight training' and 'powerlifting' which are all activities which involve training with weights. Bodybuilding has been described variously as an exercise system, a sport, an art form, a lifestyle and even as a way of life. It has in the past had more than its fair share of criticism too, its practitioners having been accused of a plethora of negative traits including narcissism, pathological compulsive behaviour, self-obsession and massive inferiority complexes!

Jamo Nazzar showing the kind of form that is needed to win a national title.

7

While there will always be arrogant, narcissistic bad mannered individuals in all sports, and indeed all walks of life they are the exception rather than the rule, and these criticisms sound increasingly hollow as ever more well-adjusted ordinary people take to the gyms in an effort to maintain or improve their health, fitness and physical appearance. It is true to say, however, that people often do things without really thinking them through and understanding why. A brief consideration of the marketing mechanism that has popularized bodybuilding and fitness as well as the psychology of training can be very illuminating.

PSYCHOLOGY AND MARKETING

Modern bodybuilding is best understood in context. It is just part of a massive global industry that has arisen in response to the insatiable demand the modern individual has to look and feel better. Capitalism and the consumer society depends to a large extent on people's dissatisfaction in order to function. People only keep buying if they feel they lack something. Marketing exists to stimulate demand, where it does not exist it is created. Utilizing much the same marketing strategies as the beauty and fashion industries, the bodybuilding, fitness and aerobics industries have enjoyed a massive growth in popularity. The canons of physical beauty and attractiveness are continually being re-established mainly through the medium of magazines with top-quality glossy photography and by the demands of the film industry for ever more perfect bodies. Most of the images of superbodies which we are continually bombarded with in our everyday lives are produced by media professionals, photographers, art directors and advertising companies. The bodies themselves are often not natural: while many are superbly trained and conditioned they are also often the product of steroid, hormone and chemical abuse, silicone implants and cosmetic surgery. The simple fact that these bodies exist, or seem to exist, however, creates or fans an already existing dissatisfaction in the mind of the average individual with his or her physical appearance.

In one of his later works on human motivation, *Beyond the Pleasure Principle*, Sigmund Freud indicated how motivation works and explained how the avoidance of displeasure is at least as powerful a motivator as the pursuit of pleasure. This goes some way to explaining why individuals who for many years have never bothered to look after their bodies begin working out. It is not so much the case that they want to have a muscular, attractive body, more that they cannot stand not having one when everyone else seems to! Common sense recognizes this too, coaches and teachers often refer to the 'carrot and the stick' as a metaphor for the motivational mechanism corresponding to the promise of reward or the threat of punishment. The media constantly bombard people with the message that exercise makes us healthy and helps us avoid illnesses which are the consequences of a sedentary lifestyle. The picture gets increasingly complicated, however, when at the same time advertisements for food, drink and tobacco make constant appeals to the hedonist in us. We are surrounded by displays of food in advertising, shopping precincts and supermarkets, presented in the most alluring, attractive ways imaginable. Comfort becomes a sort of eleventh commandment at the same time as the fashion and slimming industry conspire to make being overweight or fat into a sin, creating a dynamic tension between appetite and appearance that more and more people find increasingly difficult to keep in balance. This goes some way to explaining why many people today eat less to avoid feeling bloated and fat, as their parents did after eating a big meal, or are driven to go and work off some calories, either before or after eating, where their parents would have been content to have a nap and develop ever larger pot bellies.

Alfred Adler, a colleague and contemporary of Freud developed his own theory of human behaviour which seems particularly apposite to the psychology of bodybuilding. In Adler's view, feelings of inferiority resulting from genetic, situational or organic factors were fundamentally important in causing the small, weak and dependent child to perceive weakness as analogous to both inferiority and femininity. This resulted in The Masculine Protest, a development of the ego where striving for power and superiority were the predictable outcomes of compensation in a patriarchal society. Adler differed from Freud in that he regarded aggression (in the sense of self-assertion) and the will to power as taking precedence over sex in the motivation underlying human conduct. He also postulated that early in life the child creates 'fictions', mental constructs or working models with which he or she assembles a 'style of life'. Adler postulated in *The Neurotic Character* (1912) that behaviour and personality must be explained teleologically, in terms of a succession of subgoals coming under the dominance of, and oriented towards, the final purpose. The whole aim of the elected 'style of life' was to move from feelings of inferiority to feelings of superiority under the direction of the individual's unconscious but uniquely created self ideal.

As Adler's theories matured, his concept of striving for superiority modified into a theory of self-actualization or realization, a goal of completion which was always sought but never quite achieved. It depended too upon harmonious integration within relationships and society, it was not a process that could be undergone by the individual in isolation. One of the outcomes of this system of psychology is that the individual's personality is determined more by what goals they choose to set than the effects which their experiences have had upon them. This makes for a refreshingly optimistic and humanistic refutation of the behaviourist position, which argues that we are products of our environment and little else. Anyone familiar with Adler's work and who reads Arnold Schwarzenegger's fascinating autobiography, *Arnold, the Education of a Bodybuilder*, cannot fail to be struck by its appropriateness.

It is clear from a reading of Adler's work that an important aspect of human nature is the capacity for insecurity and the desire to relieve that insecurity. Insecurity takes many forms and the most basic is physical, which helps explain the success of the many and varied appeals which bodybuilding offers to its practitioners.

The average person taking up weight training to tone the muscles, lose some fat and generally improve his or her appearance often finds the appearance of professional and even well developed amateurs rather intimidating. A lot of people work out and train but have no desire to develop the physique of serious bodybuilders. The perfect body is very much a subjective concept and is determined in each case by the individual's personal sense of aesthetics. For those people who simply want to be bigger and more muscular the training process gives their life new meaning, a sense of growth and progression that they find very enriching. Others are reasonably happy with the way their bodies look and train to avoid the pitfalls of over-rich diets and approaching middle age, sticking to keep fit or maintenance routines. There is a place for all kinds of trainer in most gymnasiums, although some specialize for a particular kind of clientele. Of course, leaving aside all the hype, the big advantages that aerobics, bodybuilding and fitness training have as activities is that, if practised sensibly, they do help you to keep fit, healthy and looking good, as well as being enjoyable to do.

People in all cultures have been obsessed by their bodies since the human race began – painting them, stretching them, piercing them, oiling them and generally adorning and exploring their potential. Our physical being is something we all have in common and the urge towards physical development can be detected to a certain degree in all cultures. While we all have invisible interior lives consisting of thoughts, emotions and those things which make up our personalities the vehicle for the personality is the body. To a large extent in modern western thought there has been a tendency to separate mind and body, and to place mind or consciousness in a position of superiority as summed up by the French philosopher Descartes' famous declaration, 'I think therefore I am'. There is an increasing tendency to question the validity of this position and reject it. Life is experienced physically, viscerally as well as mentally. As our occupations become increasingly artificial and physically undemanding a whole host of physical activities have sprung up to redress the imbalance. The growth in popularity of activities like yoga, Tai-chi, martial arts, combat sports and a whole host of other sports in general are indicative of this trend. Our psychological, spiritual and bodily needs have to be met one way or another in order for us to have full, rich and happy lives. Bodybuilding is one of these ways.

For the cynical, the modern-day obsession with appearances, with looking young, beautiful, fit and healthy is often dismissed as vanity. It has to be admitted that there is a dangerously specious philosophy which has sprung from the world of design summed up by the phrase, 'If it looks good, it is good'. However, working out offers the individual much more than just looking good. Most people who work out regularly have a very healthy common-sense attitude and continue working out because working out does not only help to make them look good, it makes them feel good, function better and enjoy life more. The benefits and advantages of regular work outs more than compensate for the cost in time, effort and money.

HISTORY OF BODYBUILDING

The roots of bodybuilding are much older than most people think and can be traced back through history to the physical training of the various warrior castes in different primitive societies, where the need to be physically superior to one's enemies existed. Much of the Western tradition has its roots in Ancient Greek civilization. The Greeks were very much the pathfinders in the arts, science, mathematics and the humanities. The word 'gymnasium' comes from the Greek word γυμναοιον (*gumnaoion*), meaning 'to train naked'. The Greeks boxed, wrestled and held all kinds of athletic contests, the most important of which were the Olympic Games. The track and field events are the showpiece of the modern Olympics and most of the athletes have impressive physiques. There is considerable evidence to show that the Greeks used a number of different forms of weight training to improve their athletic performance. The shot-put, the hammer and the discus all involve throwing fairly weighty objects which had a more practical use than demonstrating strength by simply lifting things. In the works of Homer, Odysseus displays his strength by throwing discuses heavier than those of his enemies and defeats the giant Ajax in a wrestling match by evolving a kind of primitive judo. The discus was a natural weapon for the Greeks because Greece was a mountainous land of loose stones and rocks and those stones were readily available to pick up and throw at an enemy.

Athletes of the 6th century BC trained to develop strength and vitality by running, jumping lifting and throwing things as well as boxing and wrestling. A historian of the period, Philostratus, declared that the aim of physical training was to make the body strong and healthy and with that end in view, the athletes trained for eight or nine Olympiads, which must have guaranteed their health and vigour into their late forties and fifties at the very least!

There is evidence that the Ancient Greek athletes used hand-held weights for both running and jumping to develop everything from speed, strength and power to stamina and endurance. There are also pieces of archaeological evidence to indicate that weightlifting or strength testing by lifting rocks took place. On Mount Olympus, there is a block of red sandstone which bears an inscription saying that a hero lifted it over his head with one hand. There is also a huge block of black volcanic rock to be found in Santorini weighing 480kg, and which has an inscription dating from the 6th century BC written on it declaring, 'Eumastus son of Critobulus lifted me from the ground'.

The Roman Empire, which lay the foundations for a great deal of modern European countries, took much of its cultural and artistic inspiration from Greek civilization. One famous strongman, Milo of Croton (modern-day Calabria in Italy) is usually cited as the first case of progressive resistance weight training. As a youth around the year 558BC he began to exercise by carrying a young calf on his shoulders and to walk around a field where he lived. He did this every day for four years and as the animal grew bigger and heavier, so did Milo, until eventually he could carry a full-grown bull.

The Farnese Hercules by Glycon; an Athenian statue from the 1st century BC. *National Museum, Naples.*

Many sculptures, ceramics and friezes have survived from the time of the Greeks and Romans, depicting the kind of athletically powerful physiques that have generally been

Day by Michelangelo. *Medici Chapel, Church of San Lorenzo, Florence.*

universally admired. The 'Farnese Hercules' statue by Glycon is perhaps the best known of these in bodybuilding circles, but there are a host of others such as the 'Discobolus' or discus thrower of Myron and the 'Laocoon' of the Rhodian sculptors Polydorus, Agesander and Athenodorus. Many of the Greek heroes are archetypes which have been absorbed into the Western subconscious and continue to inspire books and films today just as they inspired the great Renaissance master, Michelangelo Buonarroti, whose heavily muscled 'Day', although unfinished, conveys a sense of power and grandeur scarcely equalled. Benvenuto Cellini, the prominent Renaissance sculptor, was another artist whose desire to create a masterpiece led him to choose a theme from Greek myth for his monumental work, the bronze 'Perseus'. What all these works have in common is a sense of muscular, masculine virility which is a physical quality – a form of beauty if you like – that has remained perennial over thousands of years.

Among the great counterforces to the Greek physical ideals in Western culture were the essentially Christian notions that the body was something base, something to be ashamed of, that asceticism was preferable to hedonism and that self-denial should be encouraged.

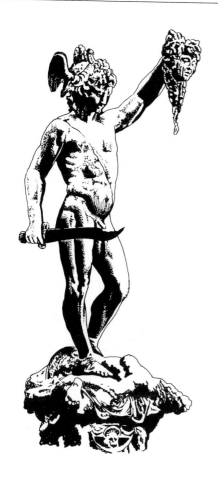

Perseus by Benvenuto Cellini, c.1550. *Loggia dei Lanzi, Piazza della Signoria, Florence.*

Baron Pierre de Coubertin revived the Olympic spirit at the end of the 19th century and set in motion the modern Olympic movement. However, there are many sports practised in different parts of the world which are not included in the Olympics. In the Basque region in Spain, one of the traditional national sports which remains widely practised is stonelifting. Ireland and Scotland are also countries with a long tradition of lifting and throwing stones in competitions of strength and power. The Highland games are still celebrated for cash prizes and many professional strongmen take part, putting the shot, throwing the hammer and tossing the caber.

History and myth are full of famous strong men, from Samson and Hercules to the Emperor Frederick the Great. One of the most outstanding physical specimens by all accounts was the Londoner Thomas Topham (*b.* 1710) whose incredible feats, in days when nothing was known of growth hormones or anabolic steroids, were recorded scientifically by a Doctor John Theophilus Desaguliers of the Royal Society. Topham's feats included a harness lift of barrels estimated at weighing 2.5 tons and witnessed by officers of the British Admiralty. Posters for his performances promised that spectators would see him bending two-inch iron bars around his neck and snapping ropes that would hold a ton weight 'with ease'. Many of these feats are recorded in wood engravings, illustrations and newspaper articles. In a London theatre he took on a line-up of six professional pugilists and wrestlers and disposed of all of them in less than three minutes 'laying them all out cold as if they were but children'. Topham weighed 196lb (89kg) and stood 6ft 6in (198cm) tall, so although a very tall man he was not massive by modern standards, but his strength and leverage were exceptional. Unfortunately, his personal life was far from happy and his wife's frequent infidelities caused him to take his own life in a fit of depression, which may indicate that he suffered from extreme hormonal imbalances.

By the end of the 18th century, many European countries had begun to give increasing importance to physical education, bodily development and manly exercises. A German teacher, Johann Gutsmuth, who wrote the *Encyclopaedia of Bodily Exercises*, is considered to be one of the pivotal figures in the popularization of physical training, as is his countryman Frederick Jahn who invented the parallel and horizontal bars and floor exercises as training disciplines that would develop into components of the sport of gymnastics. In Sweden, callisthenics became a popular form of exercising and weight training began to become increasingly popular in Great British and France. Some of these early gymnasiums dedicated to physical culture were superbly well equipped and spacious, although the majority of those training in them tended to be professional athletes. Hipolitus Triat in Paris was renowned for his superb physique and became famous as a teacher of physical culture. About 1800, the huge French Canadian Louis Cyr became famous for his prodigious feats of strength and was often referred to as the strongest man in the world.

The late 19th- and early 20th-century strong men were the first to benefit from the existence of a new technology: photography. These early strong men were the prototypes of the modern-day bodybuilders and powerlifters, men such as Eugene Sandow and Herman Goerner. These men were the exception rather than the rule and tended to work as music hall and circus performers, demonstrating their physical strength and impressive physiques to an awed public.

Sandow, whose real name was Frederick Muller (1867–1925) was of Prussian extraction and created quite a stir in Brussels by breaking a number of the then fashionable strength-testing machines situated in public places. He did this quite deliberately knowing that the machines would be repaired and that the police would be called to keep an eye on them and ensure that further vandalism did not take place. Sure enough that was what happened. When he returned and began breaking machines again he was arrested by the police. They were forced to release him when he demonstrated that he was only doing what the machines had been designed for, after inserting his money and following the printed instructions. This publicity stunt got Sandow quite a lot of work and set his career as a strongman in motion. He achieved much wider fame in 1889, however, when he challenged the famous English strongman team Samson and Cyclops to a test of strength in the Westminster Theatre in London. A masterful showman, Sandow leaped onto the stage fully dressed in a superbly tailored suit, challenged the pair, then stripped off to display his remarkable physique. He easily outdid the much larger pair's best efforts and left the theatre to a standing ovation, pursued by a mob of new fans who wanted to share his company.

Powerful muscular physiques have always attracted attention and admiration in this way. The world champion wrestler, George Hackenschmidt, 'the Russian Lion', was frequently photographed shirtless in order to display his impressive physique and many top sports stars of today appear on television advertising a whole range of goods and services and stand out on account of their impressive physiques.

Sandow became a rich man because of his physical prowess and highly developed sense of showbusiness. In 1893, he met up with the king of the showmen P.T. Barnum, who became his manager at the Chicago World's Fair. Sandow was already earning between $1,500 and $3,500 a week depending on the number of daily exhibitions he performed there. One of the spectators at the World's Fair was Bernard McFadden, a keen young bodybuilder who was inspired to dedicate himself full time to physical culture after meeting Sandow. He turned out to be a better businessman than a bodybuilder and created a financial empire out of physical culture valued at $30,000,000 mainly through his success in the field of publishing where his magazine *Physical Culture* reached a circulation of 400,000 copies.

The era of the highly paid professional strongman as performer came to an end to a certain extent because of the Industrial Revolution. As more and more people moved into the cities from the farms and began working in factories and offices, physical strength became less and less relevant in most ordinary people's eyes, and the movie industry began to have a serious impact on the music halls, the Hollywood dream factories eventually virtually putting them out of business.

The 1950s and 1960s saw a massive growth in the comic book industry with DC and Marvel comics in particular offering the new concept of the superhero to a juvenile public. In comics, graphic novels and films, the modern concept of the hero is almost always muscular in the extreme. Whether it be fiction written for children or pulp fiction written for adults, muscular, physically powerful heroes from Tarzan the Ape Man, Conan the Barbarian through to Superman, the Incredible Hulk and Judge Dredd are the order of the day. The seeds of masculine identity are planted very early and the surrounding culture ensures that they get plenty of watering and fertilizing.

Admittedly, many bodybuilders find such pulp fiction to be a source of inspiration. The most dramatic and effective cover paintings in the whole field of sword and sorcery and epic fantasy literature were painted using bodybuilders as models for the Robert E. Howard series of Conan books, which were the work of the much admired Frank Frazetta. The film 'Conan the Barbarian' was to provide Arnold Schwarzenegger (The Austrian Oak) with the vehicle he needed to become a major Hollywood film star after appearances in 'Pumping Iron', a black-and-white documentary about bodybuilding, and 'Stay Hungry' had established his star potential. In 'Stay Hungry', Arnold had to play the part of a competitive bodybuilder, just as Dave Draper did in the earlier beach movie 'Making Waves'.

The Austrian Oak is by no means the only person to make the transition from bodybuilder to film star. The most enduring of all the fictional and mythical heroes has been Hercules, the archetypal strongman, and there has been a plethora of films which have featured bodybuilders playing the part of the Ancient Greek demigod, such as Reg Park, Steve Reeves and more recently Lou Ferringo. Sylvester Stallone who shot to stardom when he wrote and starred in the film 'Rocky' has had an impressive and highly successful career. Stallone had a good average physique as a result of working out with weights when he started, but as a consequence of studio demands for leaner, bigger more muscular bodies he devoted himself wholeheartedly to developing his physique following the advice and guidance of a number of top bodybuilders along the way, notably Franco Columbo. Stallone's film career is an interesting document of how bodybuilding training can over the years completely transform a physique. The demand for fit, muscular bodies in the 1980s and 1990s has meant that whole generations of would-be actors and actresses have devoted huge amounts of energy to training and dietary regimes as an investment in their most valuable asset – themselves. The lean, muscular, well-toned body is one of the great objects of desire in modern society, so much so that for many people it has become an obsession. The important thing is that the obsession should be a healthy one.

The most successful bodybuilder turned film star is beyond any shadow of a doubt the great Arnold Schwarzenegger, the photogenic Austrian-American who combines an awesome physique with great personal charisma.

15

'Arnie' has been a source of inspiration to whole generations of bodybuilders, epitomizing the notion of success through hard work. It is important to realize, however, that the positive results of well-planned bodybuilding regimes are not just cosmetic. Olympic and professional athletes the world over have turned to weight training, using tried-and-tested bodybuilding techniques as a supplementary form of conditioning training to help them get stronger and faster. Any body can be improved by a well-designed training programme and an appropriate diet. The superbly fit world heavyweight boxing champion Evander Holyfield who was essentially a pumped-up cruiserweight sought the advice and assistance of the great, eight times 'Mr Olympia' Lee Haney when he wanted to make more lasting gains to increase his muscular bodyweight. In spite of numerous setbacks, his diligence eventually bore fruit when he stunned the boxing world by winning the world title for a third time. Holyfield, a 15–1 underdog, defeated the fearsome Mike Tyson in the eleventh round of an epic contest where his newly gained strength and weight made a crucial difference to his remarkable victory.

BODYBUILDING TODAY

Bodybuilding today is not a beauty contest, although there are more and more contests of this type for men and the competitors invariably work out in order to stay in the shape required to compete and have some hope of winning. Bodybuilding is about who has the most muscle, the lowest body fat, the best definition, the most pleasing symmetry and the most impressive posing routine. As greater numbers of people come into the activity, there is increasingly a trend towards a diversification of governing bodies, organizations and categories. Not everyone wants to be as big as top professionals like Dorian Yates, Paul Dillet or Lou Ferringo. To keep people motivated beyond the idea of just looking good – which is pretty subjective – different categories have emerged, partly as a result of cross-fertilization between bodybuilding and other forms of physical training such as aerobics. Fitness contests for both sexes have sprung up which have as much in common with women's beauty contests as with hard-core bodybuilding.

Activities which in the past were forms of training devised to get people in shape for sports or physically challenging roles have become sports in themselves. Athletes, footballers, boxers and a host of other sportsmen and women have used weight training, stretching and aerobic activities as part of the physical preparation they need to take part in their given sports. These forms of training though have become more popular than some of the sports they were designed to serve, partly because they have an inherently competitive component and a very low skill factor. Virtually anybody can do them and make measurable improvements.

No account of the popularization of bodybuilding and fitness would be complete without mentioning Joe Weider and *Muscle and Fitness*, the magazine which helped popularize bodybuilding on a massive scale. A study of the evolution of *Muscle and Fitness* over a period of twelve years (from 1977 to 1989) demonstrates how some remarkable changes in social attitudes and what was considered acceptable were engineered. The marketing of bodybuilding as a sport turns into the marketing of bodybuilding as lifestyle and in the process the strategies used to manufacture glamour become apparent. In June 1978 *Muscle Builder and Power* as the magazine was then called was a 148-page black-and-white magazine comprising a four-page full-colour wraparound section, with sixteen pages of colour spread through the front and rear of the magazine and a sixteen-page full-colour central insert. Apart from the cover, the other thirty-five colour pages were all advertising. The covers in this period tended to be photographs of top bodybuilders, which made the magazine quite an anomaly on the newsstands, given that it was a minority sport. It contrasts dramatically with the February 1987 cover shot taken nine years later, which depicts an entirely more complex gender display, which would be developed over the intervening years.

The sixteen page insert in the June 1978 issue was in effect a catalogue of bodybuilding training equipment, food supplements and associated merchandise. All of the editorial photography was black and white. The use of black-and-white photography was originally determined by considerations of cost, but one interesting effect which this generated was to give the editorial a documentary feel. Black and white was always traditionally the medium of news and reportage and its use gave the articles a certain authority and authenticity. The content of the photographs is thematically exclusive, featuring bodybuilders in one of three situations: training, competing or posing artistically for portrait type photographs. Interestingly out of a total of 206 black-and-white editorial photographs only six contain women and of those, three show women congratulating a competition-winning bodybuilder and two are delegates at a bodybuilding conference. In 1978, the world of bodybuilding was almost exclusively a man's world.

There is one photograph which in retrospect can be seen to be the most important because it was the progenitor of a whole design and photographic strategy. Though remarkably simple and indeed commonplace outside of bodybuilding, it would prove to be extremely effective in promoting the activity.

The picture shows a young Arnold Schwarzenegger advertising three waist shaper rubber undersuits. A bikini-clad girl poses with him, caressing his hair as both smile into the camera. It was perhaps the first glimmer of awareness in the publishers of a need to communicate something about the sexuality of bodybuilders.

Among the image problems traditionally associated with bodybuilding, drugs, narcissism and homosexuality were probably the most serious obstacles to its popularization. The narcissism inherent in bodybuilding was – and frequently still is – both obvious and extremely difficult to deny. A regular advertisement in the magazines declaring 'Watch your muscles grow!' is fairly representative of the self-absorbed nature of the activity.

The charismatic Arnold Schwarzenegger was to become the solution to many of problems associated with the sport's image. He became the apotheosis of the bodybuilding ideal and appeared in almost every issue during this period, when his career in acting was just beginning to develop. He went on to become the biggest star in Hollywood in terms of box office receipts and together with Sylvester Stallone, is the ultimate vindication for the hyperbole made on behalf of the bodybuilding lifestyle.

John Berger wrote in *Ways of Seeing*. 'The purpose of publicity is to make the spectator marginally dissatisfied with his present way of life. Not with the way of life of society, but his own within it. It suggests that if he buys what it is offering, his life will become better. It offers him an improved alternative to what he is.' This is almost exactly what the bodybuilding lifestyle proposes, but in order to make the proposal seem feasible, it had to construct a whole belief system to persuade the reader that this was a valid proposition. By August 1978 the coverline of *Muscle and Power* boasted 'fifty colour pages', fourteen of which were devoted to editorial photography. The photographs were in turn informed by the rhetoric of the editorial copy and the aggrandizement which ensues transfers to the advertisements. Page 2 has an advertisement for a Weider Power-X rubber exerciser and features 'Mr Olympia' Frank Zane in a carefully lit shot which presents his physique to its best advantage. Page 46 is a similar photograph featuring the champion in a different pose and which accompanies an article about his training methods. This piece details the process whereby he sculpts his body like an artist and is entitled 'Zane's Quest for Perfection'. It is just one of many editorials where the bodybuilder is represented as hero, champion, sculptor, philosopher, poet or some other 'greater than the normal type of human' in unashamed flourishes of rhetoric. The usual articles and photographs are repeated, grids comparing competitors to give an impression of innumerable highly trained bodies and to create the impression of a worldwide phenomenon.

It is important to understand the effect that repeated exposure to these kind of images and articles has, and the way in which a very particular context is established for interpreting the plethora of visual images. The magazine articulates a belief system, an ideology – it is bodybuilding's propaganda.

Describing the editorial content of a bodybuilding magazine as propaganda may seem extreme, the term is generally reserved for politically motivated communication. However, it is no exaggeration. In later issues the new reader is immediately struck by the number of glossy colour photographs of muscular bodies and may, depending upon personal preference, admire, be repulsed, or remain unmoved by the spectacle. Many claim to be inspired by reading the magazines, but some find them depressing because of the gulf between what they see in them and the reality of their own bodies.

The editorial tone throughout the late 1970s was self-reflective, reconsidering the sport's purpose and direction and reassuring the reader endlessly. The editorials are remarkable for the success which they have had in propagating the ideology of the bodybuilding industry. Consider this passage from an editorial in the June 1979 issue, where the new editorial policy on cover design using portrait shots instead of bodybuilders in posing trunks is used, to explain the magazine's mission.

'For *Muscle Builder* to grow, it has to broaden its appeal. That's why we've included the section on bodybuilding for women. For a long time muscles were considered grotesque. There was a lot of ignorance. Women didn't like men with overly muscular physiques. Because of this *Muscle Builder* was restricted in its audience. Our readers were muscle fanatics, members of a special subculture of bodybuilders who understood what it was all about. But all that is changing now. First there was "Pumping Iron". Then Lou Ferringo starred in the "Incredible Hulk". As a general awareness of physical fitness swept the country all the major magazines began running stories on bodybuilding. People began flocking to gyms; doctors, lawyers, businessmen, students, housewives. Many of them read *Muscle Builder*, along with athletes, coaches and physical fitness instructors. That's one reason for the change in cover style. When most people see a bodybuilder posing they think it's an ego trip. They see someone completely absorbed in self interest and narcissism. A photo like that on the cover will turn them off, With a head shot what they see is a personality, someone they can relate to. Instead of a muscle freak we're introducing them to a human being.'

Joe Weider's success is both remarkable and undeniable. He is the patriarch of bodybuilding, was the chairman of the International

Federation of Body Builders (IFBB) for many years, editor, publisher and entrepreneur, he is also the magazine's chief advertiser. His brother Ben Weider is now the President of the IFBB and Joe Weider limits himself to organizing the most prestigious bodybuilding competitions in the world. The 'Mr Olympia', the 'Mr Senior Olympia' and the 'Miss Olympia', as well as running a publishing empire that includes *Muscle and Fitness, Flex* (for the hard-core bodybuilder), *Shape* for women and *Men's Fitness*. In the late 1970s he also began selling vast quantities of food supplements, training equipment and expertise. The magazine featured champions who advertised their individual training courses, revealing their secrets and became celebrities in the process.

By April 1980, the strategy of using portrait shots of famous bodybuilders' faces had been abandoned. Couples began to appear; men and women training together, to 'tone up' and 'develop energy'. A relatively 'slim' type of bodybuilder, Steve Davis, appeared in two editorial pieces, training with a woman partner in one and as an illustration to an article on 'Sex and Bodybuilding'. Lou Ferringo who played the Incredible Hulk on television and later Hercules and Sinbad in the movies, was pictured embracing wife Carla. Boyer Coe, another champion bodybuilder, was featured getting married to girlfriend Valerie. Frank Zane appeared with wife Christine in a bikini. The heterosexual dimension of bodybuilding was being clearly established in a very pointed manner. The features included articles on bodybuilding as lifestyle medicine, using exercise to overcome stress and enjoying healthy living.

By November 1983, the new cover style, which has endured until the present was established and the magazine had a new masthead: *Muscle and Fitness*, with the word 'Fitness' larger and foregrounded over 'Muscle'. The new cover style featured a young handsome body-builder in a fairly relaxed pose accompanied by a beautiful, stereotypically sexy, bunny-girl type woman. Inside the magazine has changed considerably too and now exhibits extremely high-quality production values, full-colour printing on 242 pages of which half is advertising. It continues to project an unwavering, sustained conviction as to the benefits of the bodybuilding lifestyle and contains lots of photographs of men and women lifting weights and flexing pumped-up muscles. One of the remarkable things about the magazine as an environment is that it is increasingly difficult to separate what it is that distinguishes the advertisements from the editorial because 99 per cent of the time the aims and content of both are the same: to sell the idea of bodybuilding. Joe Weider succeeded brilliantly in what he set out to do and made it possible for millions to feel good about becoming involved in bodybuilding.

2 Beginning Bodybuilding

BUILDING THE BODY YOU WANT

Every day, millions of people worldwide go to gymnasiums and health clubs to work out. Many of these people go training with a view to improving their fitness, their appearance and their health. In order to reach these goals they usually set themselves goals which have a lot in common with the bodybuilder. They want leaner, more muscular, better proportioned, attractive bodies. In spite of this, they do not see themselves as bodybuilders and indeed many people now involved in competitive bodybuilding did not go into training initially with a view to being competitive bodybuilders. Often this is because the trainees are so far away from resembling anything like a competitive bodybuilder that the thought hardly crosses their minds.

Most people start out wanting to be bigger, stronger, leaner, fitter or a combination of these things. Many are embarrassed to say that they are doing bodybuilding initially and prefer to describe what they do as weight training or keeping fit, not being really sure what bodybuilding consists of. Teenagers are often an exception to this rule. They have often been introduced to bodybuilding via the magazines and have clearer idea of the kind of body they want, envisaging themselves as bodybuilders from day one. For the majority, it is usually only after a few years have passed that this reticence disappears. Then the results of the training are obvious for all to see, in the individual's improved body. The role shyness passes and they find themselves saying quite happily and unselfconsciously that they do bodybuilding. In fact, sooner or later it becomes something that they pride themselves on, a topic of conversation and something that they feel makes them more interesting and complete as people. Beginners often worry about what people will think of them if they say they are doing bodybuilding, that the fact that they want to improve their bodies is akin to an admission of weakness and inferiority and so on. These are phantoms that should be dispelled right from the start. Do bodybuilding because you want to; because it makes you look and feel better and you enjoy it. Always remember, you do not have to justify wanting to improve yourself to anyone.

The Age Factor

One of the most important factors to take into account when starting training is age and your current physical state. Children undergoing puberty should be closely supervised if training with weights, as their joints and bones are still soft and growing and they are very susceptible to injury and damage which may not show up until later on in life. Correct form and light poundages should generally be the order of the day for them and they should always be supervised.

Teenagers who take up bodybuilding can make excellent improvements very quickly, mainly because the body is still producing fairly large amounts of growth hormone naturally. Many trainers regard sixteen or seventeen to be an ideal age to start for maximum growth. Men and women in their early twenties are in their physical prime and can usually get into shape fairly quickly and make further progress without any great difficulty. A medical check up before embarking on a training regime is always a good idea.

The same applies to over thirty-fives starting to train for the first time or returning to training after a long lay off. Ex-sportsmen and ex-athletes should be particularly careful not to let themselves get carried away by their enthusiasm as they are likely to have a competitive nature and may tend to overdo it initially, especially if they used to train at a high level. Training should be a gradual process for people over thirty and progress will occur at a natural, reasonable pace without injuries and setbacks that result from overdoing it initially.

Setting Goals

Almost everyone who begins training with weights in a gymnasium does so either because they are not happy with the way their body looks or because they have to get physically better conditioned in order to achieve a better performance in their chosen sport. What people in both categories have to have in common if they are to make real progress is a definite goal. This can be anything from wanting to increase upper body strength to the point where they can do a 300lb bench press, or build a pair of 20 inch upper arms, or to lose 20lb of fat to get into a pair of jeans that used to fit. People who are more into serious bodybuilding may have more difficulty in attaining goals such as wanting to win a local, regional, area or national championship. In many ways the

most positive aspect of competing, even if you are never going to win, is that it gives you a focus for your training and helps you to reach your maximum potential.

Goal-setting is very important and one way to keep a record of your goals and your progress towards them is the training diary. A well-kept training diary should contain a daily log of training done, sets, repetitions poundages, rest periods, time taken to complete workouts, dietary habits, vitamin supplementation, strength and energy levels and should record any relevant changes.

It is important to set short term goals as well as long-term ones. Short-term goals give you something immediate to aim at and train for, and make training interesting, helping to keep you motivated. Short-term goals can be as simple as wanting to increase your strength or aerobic fitness allowing you to increase the intensity of future workouts. This can involve simple challenges like trying to do two more repetitions in a given exercise, or the same number with a heavier weight, or doing an extra ten minutes on the stationary bike. Some bodybuilders like to monitor their strength gains. These are to some extent related to changes in physiques and they may do strength tests two or three times a year to get an idea of their maximum poundages in the basic power exercises like the bench press, squat and deadlift. They then use these as a guide to calculate the sort of poundages they need to be using to continue making good gains. If you never increase the intensity of the exercise by either increasing the weight and/or repetitions or decreasing the rest periods, the muscles get used to the weight and growth ceases.

Training, Diet and Recovery

For those people who really want to do bodybuilding and are not just interested in keeping fit, toning up or improving their sports performance it is important to realize that what goes on in the gym is probably less than 50 per cent of the process. In order for muscles to grow, the body needs to be both fed and rested. The process is relatively straightforward. High-intensity exercise has a catabolic effect on muscle, breaking it down. Eating – feeding the body – then provides the organism with the necessary proteins and amino acids to replenish and restore the muscles, which adapt to the demands placed on them by exercise, by growing bigger and stronger. This anabolic phase is the body's normal adaptive response to intense exercise. Of course, the body needs fats carbohydrates, vitamins, minerals and water as well, in order to function healthily and ensure that its energy systems are adequately topped up. Glycogen is produced by the liver after eating and stored in the muscles, exercise uses up the glycogen. After exercise, it has to be replenished.

Consistency

In the early stages of training one of the most important factors is consistency. Variety is another important principle, but it does not become so important until later on. Consistency, however, does not mean training flat out every day. It is important to monitor what effect training has on your body. Be alert to the dangers of overtraining, spending too long in the gym, doing too many sets and reps and not growing. Many intermediate bodybuilders stop making progress because they increase the amount and frequency of exercise they do rather than the intensity of the exercise. Worse still, they do not allow themselves sufficient recovery time between training sessions, so the body does not have time to recover and grow.

SOMATOTYPE

All bodies are slightly different but there is a system of classification of anatomic type which was devised by Doctor William H. Sheldon of Harvard University, who was an expert in anthropometry (the measurement of the different parts of the body). The term 'somatotype' is synonymous with body type and refers to the physical characteristics of individual bodies. Sheldon identified three extreme types after examining thousands of students:

- The term 'endomorph' describes the pear-shaped pudgy type who tends to carry a fair amount of fat, giving a soft, rounded appearance.
- 'Mesomorph' is the term used to describe the broad-shouldered, narrow waisted, athletic muscular individual.
- 'The ectomorph' on the other hand is the lean, nervous type who carries less muscle and fat.

These terms describe the extremes of the observed physical types encountered in the study. Sheldon conceived a nine-point scale to determine where any given individual would fall within this system of somatotyping, based on height and weight, bone size, limb length, and muscle and fat ratios. Somatotype should be thought of as a continuum rather than as a fixed system. All bodies can change and many physical types can incline from one to another. The truth is, however, that you are born with a particular, genetically predetermined somatotype which will play an enormous role in dictating how your body responds to diet and exercise.

Genetic Factors

Bodybuilding is an activity where genetic factors play an extremely important part in determining how fast and how far people

Brian Buchanan smiling after his Amateur Mr Universe win.

bodybuilder were to retire and in an extreme case scenario, stop training and eat everything in sight, his or her body type – however benevolent his or her genetics – would rapidly move towards endomorphy. Choosing to keep a close watch on diet but not training to hold the muscle would result in a gradual loss of muscular bulk and a move towards ectomorphy.

Basketball is a game where height is an advantage. Consequently, many top basketball players are mesomorphs inclined towards ectomorphy. If they were initially very skinny and had built themselves up through training and intelligent diet and supplementation, they may be described as ectomorphs inclining towards mesomorphy. These are the kind of people who, if they stop eating and training adequately, rapidly lose the muscle they have gained.

A very fat and flabby, out-of-condition endomorph can usually make good progress by training and dieting. Indeed, some notable bodybuilding stars, such as the blonde Californian Dave Draper were endomorphs who learned to harness their natural tendency to put on weight to good effect by controlling their diet and metabolism to gain muscle and burn fat. The endomorph's problem is that there is a tendency to put on fat with ease, usually with a low tolerance to using up carbohydrates. Some people, normally ectomorphs – the naturally lean type who have great difficulty putting on muscle – are dubbed 'hard gainers' in bodybuilding circles. This is because they apparently do everything right and yet seem to make very slow progress and the slightest deviation from diet or lapse in training sees them lose ground with astonishing speed in their quest to build a better body. Others, especially those who have been fat or obese as youngsters and tend towards endomorphy also have to fight an uphill battle. They tend to

can improve their bodies. Genetics to a large extent determine the muscles' capacity for growth and size and predetermine their shape. As has already been indicated, no two bodies are identical and in many respects differences in genetics make bodybuilding an unequal arena. However, this is true of many other sports too, so bodybuilding is by no means unique in this respect.

There are some important variables. Top bodybuilding champions in peak condition are pure mesomorphs. However, if a champion gain weight relatively easily, but unfortunately put on fat more easily than muscle. Low carbohydrate tolerance or incorrect diet for their particular body types may mean they always have to fight a permanent battle to keep the flab and fat from obscuring and hiding their hard-won muscle, permanently watching the calories and composition of their diets and doing lots of aerobics. On the positive side they can get very strong and fit as a result of their efforts, but will generally find it easier to stay fit and strong than lean and muscular. The natural endomorph really has to be re-educated as to how and what to eat in order to avoid the dangers of obesity in later years.

The type of mesomorph who for many years tended not to come into bodybuilding because they were naturally muscular and inclined to be involved in sports that kept them in fine shape anyway can make astonishingly rapid progress. Benevolent genetics and good metabolisms combine to make them formidable as bodybuilders. They seem to grow just by touching the weights. Some have relatively poor exercise technique, seem to eat more or less what they feel like, train moderately hard and grow visibly by the week. The genetically gifted can make the kind of transformation in their bodies in three to five years that might take the hard gainer ten to fifteen years – and with considerably less suffering. When such individuals combine the necessary discipline, determination and desire they usually become champions.

COMPETITION

The important thing to keep in mind, however, is that *everyone* can improve and make themselves look and feel better. The vast majority of people working out in gyms across the world do not compete in bodybuilding competitions, nor do they have any desire to be as big as Dorian Yates. Entering contests is a difficult but highly rewarding experience if you go about it the right way. Even for amateurs it requires years of training, sensible eating and tremendous self-discipline, especially in the final three months or so. The process of doing the hard work and applying your knowledge and discipline to the task of getting into the best possible shape is what really matters, not whether you look bigger or better than all the rest and win on the day.

Winning is a great experience, but it should not become the be-all and end-all as it does for many people. In the final analysis the important thing is not whether you win or not – there could always be someone who has trained better, or longer, or dieted more strictly or simply has had superior genetics from day one. Competition is about coming in on the day looking the best that you possibly can without having resorted to anabolic steroids, growth hormone, testosterone or other potentially dangerous drugs. The real competition is with yourself.

WHERE TO TRAIN

The Home as a Gym

Many people start out in bodybuilding using a set of second-hand weights and training at home. When talking about the home gym here we are not talking about a millionaire's purpose-built and designed room which in some cases are as well equipped as commercial gymnasiums. The typical home gym is someone's back garden, garage, spare bedroom or scullery which gets converted for training purposes, usually temporarily. In fact there is nothing to stop you having some excellent workouts in this kind of a home gym, even with quite rudimentary equipment. In many working-class communities sons learned from fathers and elder brothers in this way; physical training was a normal part of growing up before the advent of colour television. A barbell with about a hundred kilograms in discs, collars to prevent the weights from sliding off the bar, a pair of dumb-bells with collars so that you can change the weights, and a bench – and you have all you need to get into good shape. Second hand, it probably does not amount to much more than a yearly membership in many commercial gyms.

Few people have the space available for a permanent home gym and often for keen beginners it is a question of putting the equipment in a cupboard and moving rugs and furniture in order to get it out and train. Some prefer to train in their garages, or in back gardens where they get the benefit of fresh air but have to put up with the changes in the weather.

There are advantages and disadvantages to training at home as compared with going to commercial gyms, sports centres and the like:

Advantages
• Time and money saved by not having to travel.
• You can train when it suits you.
• You never have to find the money to go.
• It is easy to get friends or family involved.
• You can do what you want without interference or disturbance.

Disadvantages
• The nuisance factor if your training annoys other members of your family or neighbours.
• Getting equipment out and putting it away.
• Training alone can be boring, you tend to run out of ideas and motivation.
• No social element.
• No feedback as to how your training is going.

• Safety can be a problem, training without a spotter makes certain important exercises inadvisable.
• There is no exposure to other ideas and ways of training so you may not learn as much as you would in a commercial gym or sports centre.

Bearing all of the above in mind, excellent results can still be obtained in an intelligently set out home gym.

Commercial Gyms – the Right One

If you decide to take bodybuilding more seriously, it is doubtful that you will be content to train at home indefinitely. Finding the right gym is one of the most important elements in achieving your bodybuilding goals. There is a huge variety of places offering access to fitness, bodybuilding and weight training equipment including private health clubs, the YMCA, local sports and leisure centres, fitness centres and the traditional but fast disappearing hardcore spit, sweat and sawdust gyms.

More expensive does not always mean better. The most important thing about any gym is that you should be able to train there. It is worth travelling around and seeing as many different gyms as possible, compare prices, equipment, opening times, additional facilities, kinds of tuition or instruction offered and even the intangible qualities that make all the difference, like the atmosphere and the people who are training there. Watch out for the telltale signs of lack of interest on the part of the instructor, broken equipment that is waiting to be repaired, the state of the showers, changing rooms and whether the hygiene levels are up to scratch. You will be spending a fair bit of time in the gym so you should go somewhere you are going to enjoy being and where you do not find the people too difficult to get on with.

TRAINING PARTNERS

While it may be an exaggeration to say that good training partners are worth their weight in gold there is no denying that the right person can make an enormous difference to your workouts for a whole host of reasons. The key word is 'good'. Some people are not too serious about what they do when they go to the gym, really, they do not train – they go there for a chat and a bit of exercise and to see friends and acquaintances. Your training partner should have similar goals and attitudes to training to you; if not, it is unlikely to work out very well.

You and your training partner can help each other in all sorts of areas: motivation, encouragement, feedback, criticism, support and just having fun together as you go through your workouts. No two people are exactly alike and often one partner may be stronger on pushing movements while the other is stronger on pulling movements. One may have stronger legs, the other a more powerful upper body. This can be just what you need to bring your flagging muscle groups up to scratch – regular hard training in competition with someone who is a little stronger than you are, who wants to train the body parts you might be inclined to leave alone if you were left to your own devices. You can complement one another if you have different skills or knowledge. Perhaps you know more about diet than your partner but he knows more about flexibility. Share your knowledge and experiences and you both benefit. Training with someone else often makes it easier to establish a routine. If you are in two minds about going training one day because you feel like watching TV or going to the cinema, having to turn up because your partner is waiting for you can be very good from the point of view of self-imposed discipline.

Training alone can be very difficult especially if you do not have clearly defined goals.

WORKOUT GEAR

Wearing the right gear is very important when working out, but the majority of people do not dress adequately when they go into the gym. Safety, comfort and mobility are the most important considerations. Do not wear tight-fitting clothes as they are likely to tear. Dress according to the temperature; in cold weather it is especially important to be well wrapped up to assist with an effective warm up.

Boots

All bodybuilders are well advised to invest in a good pair of weightlifting boots of the type which have a slightly built-up heel that provides a brace for the ankles. These are designed to help the person wearing them to keep good posture and balance when exercising. The soles of these boots should be non-slip, although the gymnasium flooring may be as important a factor in many cases.

Belts

A vital piece of equipment is a weightlifting belt. Such belts tend to be made of leather and are about three to four inches wide at the back with a narrower strap and buckle at the front. More modern nylon belts are longer lasting and less likely to rot as a result of sweating profusely and general wear and tear. These are becoming increasingly available and are growing in popularity. The belt provides support for the lower back in those exercises where you stand up and a weight is lifted overhead (such as military press) and in heavy pulling exercises like the deadlift and power clean, it is essential. In back squats, its main function is to support the trunk and midsection and so prevent pulled abdominals, strains, hernias and ruptures which can befall even the most advanced trainers when using heavy weights. Olympic and powerlifters frequently use strong supportive knee wraps to help the joints cope with the tremendous pressure put on them by the enormous poundages they work with in exercises like the squat. If you decide to use wraps be careful not to put them on too tight or too slack.

Safety

Great care must be taken when heavy weights are being handled because the greater the weight, the higher the possibility of injury. All training programmes should begin with moderate poundages and the intensity of the sets should be gradually increased. Attempting to train with heavy poundages too soon is counterproductive – adequate foundation training should be done first. Chronic muscular soreness, or stiffness, lasting more than two or three days, is an indication that overtraining of the too-much-too-soon variety has taken place.

EXERCISES

Warming-up and Stretching

Warming-up and stretching are often grouped together because they are often done together, but they are in fact quite different activities. Pure warm up can involve doing jogging, skipping, static bike, rowing machine, stair climber or any other kind of aerobic exercise. Some people find it helpful to run through the movements of the various exercises with just an empty bar to prepare the muscles for the specific movements they will be making.

Stretching is a more complicated process than just warming up and the tendency to overdo it must be resisted as it can easily lead to injury. Martial artists and yoga practitioners have incredible flexibility but it normally takes many years of specialized training to develop.

Stretching should be done slowly and gradually, and the temptation to stretch as far as other people should be strongly resisted. Overenthusiastic stretching can easily cause pulled muscles and similar injuries.

Flexibility is one of the basic components of all-round fitness and anyone who does bodybuilding ought to do stretching to avoid developing a body with the tensed-up muscle-bound look. Stretching promotes suppleness in the muscles. Supple muscles allow for greater range of movement, reduce the likelihood of injury and improve the individual's capacity for making relaxed and fast movements. Lengthening the muscles as you train them can assist with a fuller, more complete development and ultimately with a more impressive, athletic looking physique.

Stretching Exercises

Stretching can be done at any time of day and should always be done in a gradual fashion. Being in a rush to stretch out can lead to pulled muscles and other problems. There are many different stretching techniques: dynamic, ballistic, isometric, proprioceptive neuromuscular facilitation (PNF) and passive stretching.

Passive stretching is the kind recommended for bodybuilders, as it is least likely to cause injury and will provide as much flexibility as you will ever need. Passive stretching technique involves using gravity, the weight of the body or a partner to help stretch the muscles. It is very important to understand the role of pain in stretching. It is neither desirable nor necessary, but very easy to experience! This is vitally important especially for intermediate and advanced bodybuilders who have considerable experience of pain from years of training but who may be less familiar with stretching techniques and methods. There is no need to feel a burn. Stretching should be a gentle, opening and relaxing experience for your body, not further punishment. The

Toe-touching (hamstring stretch).

Calf stretch.

following stretches can all be done on their own as a daily routine or incorporated into a warm-up and cool-down routine before and after working out.

Toe-touching (Hamstring Stretch)

This first exercise is to stretch the backs of the legs, the hamstrings, hips and lower spine.

Standing feet shoulder-width apart, keep the legs straight and breathe in, then bend slowly forwards at the waist, touching your finger tips on the floor. More supple individuals can put the palms of their hands flat on the floor and touch their forehead to their knees. Slowly breathe out to a count of five and straighten up again, keeping the legs straight, breathing in as you do so. Try to bend from the hips, and keep the lower back flat when you go down and lift yourself from the lower back as you straighten up.

Do exactly the same movement as outlined above, but with the feet together instead of being shoulder width apart. Hold the stretch for ten seconds before moving into the next position.

Calf Stretch

From the bent-over position, keeping the legs straight and the feet together with the heels flat on the floor. Walk forwards on your hands until you feel the stretch in your calves. Breathe normally and hold the stretch for ten seconds, then move into the next position.

Lunge (Hips and Legs)

From the calf stretch, bring your left foot forwards and take your right foot back, allowing your hips to lower until you are in a lunging position. The right (forward) foot can be placed between the hands or outside the right hand if you prefer. Let the hips sink as low as possible and feel the stretch in the

Lunge (hips and legs).

Abdominal stretch.

hips, groin and legs. Hold the stretch for ten seconds, breathing normally; then reverse the position of the feet, stretching the legs and hips on the other side, and then move into the next position.

Abdominal Stretch

Supporting your weight on your hands, bring both feet together in a press-up position and lower your hips so that your lower back bends and your body forms a bow. This stretches the front of the body, the muscles that link the legs to the pelvis and the abdomen. Locking out the arms and looking directly upwards increases the stretching effect. Hold the stretch for ten seconds and move into the next position.

Upper Back Stretch

From the prone position, shift your weight back onto your knees and allow your hips to come down until you are sitting on or between your feet. Your arms should remain outstretched in front of you. Lower your head and feel the stretch in the upper back and latissimus dorsi muscles. Breathe normally throughout the movement and hold the stretch for ten seconds before moving into the next position.

Front Body Stretch

Remain on your knees and come up into a sitting position. Put the palms of your hands on your heels, and push with your arms and legs so that your body forms an arch. Remember to breathe normally and do not strain. This is a good stretch for the whole front of the body, including the chest, shoulders, abdominals, hip, groin and thigh muscles. It stretches the biceps if you straighten the arms and lock the elbows. After holding the stretch for ten seconds, move into the next position.

Upper back stretch.

Front body stretch.

Shoulder and Lat Stretch

Stand up and bring your hands together in front of your chest as if you were about to pray. Lift your arms straight over your head and reach up with your joined hands as high as you can, breathing in as you do so. Continue to breathe in for about five seconds as you hold the stretched position. You should feel the stretch in your shoulders and upper back

31

Shoulder and lat stretch.

as well as the whole spine. Then begin to breathe out. Bring the arms down in front of you as you finish breathing out. The feet should be together and the body perfectly straight throughout this exercise.

Shoulder Joint Mobilizers

The next part of the stretching sequence emphasizes the shoulder area because so many people who train with weights have shoulder problems at different times.

Standing with the feet shoulder-width apart, lift your arms above your head and bend the left arm at the elbow. Grasp the left elbow with your right hand and gently pull the arm so that the left biceps goes behind your head, stretching the upper back and shoulder area. Repeat with the opposite arm.

Standing with your back to a column, upright, corner or wall twist at the waist and reach behind you, straightening your arm and opening up the chest area, taking hold of the column. Allow your upper body to slowly twist back into a forwards-facing position and feel the stretch in the pectoral and deltoid tie in and biceps as well as the back. Breathe normally and hold for ten seconds. Then do the other side.

Facing the column, reach up and place your forearm flat against the column. Step forward and lower your bodyweight without allowing the forearm to move, until you feel the stretch in the pectoral and deltoid. Breathe normally, hold the stretch for ten seconds, and repeat on the opposite side.

Stand sideways on to the column and bend at the waist laterally, grabbing hold of it with both hands. Push with both arms and stretch the latissimus dorsi muscles. Hold the stretch for ten seconds then turn around and repeat on the opposite side.

Shoulder joint mobilizers (1) and (2).

Lat stretch.

The above routine would take less than ten minutes to do and would be adequate stretching for an upper body workout. If combined with a few minutes' skipping or exercise bike, it should see you well-warmed up to start lifting weights for an upper body training session. If the workout was to concentrate on legs the following exercises could be added to the stretching routine.

Deep Squat with Feet Wide Apart (Hips and Quadriceps)

Stand with the feet more than shoulder-width apart, keeping a straight back. Turn the feet outwards, and slowly lower yourself down into a deep-squat position. Relax the leg muscles. Feel how the hip and knee joints align, and which muscles are stretched. Stay in this relaxed stretched position for ten seconds, breathing normally. Then, without bouncing, slowly tense the quadriceps and hip muscles and push yourself upright, keeping the back as straight as possible in a sort of super-slow squat without weight. This is a very useful way to prepare the legs for the stresses of squatting with weights.

Seated Stretching for Legs

Sit down with the weight on the buttock bones (if you feel like you are going to fall backwards, it is because your centre of gravity is not over the buttock bones) and open your legs as wide as is comfortably possible. Keep the feet angled at 90 degrees to the floor and bend forwards at the hips, sliding your hands down your legs as far as you can or until you reach your feet. Then twist at the waist until you are facing your left foot and bend forwards. Keep the knee straight and the toes pointed as far as you can or until your chest touches the knee. Hold the stretch for ten seconds then repeat on the opposite side. With these seated stretches breathe out as you bend and make the stretching movement, and breathe in as you straighten up.

Other useful variations involve doing the same movement with the leg folded in so that the foot of the bent leg is flush against the straight leg, and the hurdler's stretch position. The hurdler's stretch is so called because it is the position those athletes competing in that event take when they actually perform the hurdling action. The rear leg is bent and tucked in with the heel behind the buttock, just as it is when the hurdler lifts it out of the way to avoid clipping the hurdle.

Seated stretching for legs (1) and (2), with (3), (4) and (5) overleaf.

Stretching is a good exercise habit to develop, but like most things moderation is called for. Getting carried away and doing too much can leave you feeling as stiff and sore the following day as a session of heavy squats! In the early stages of training, ten seconds per stretch is more than enough. You could even break it down into two five-second stretches if you preferred. Later, when you are better conditioned and more supple you can do more, but build up slowly. You do not need the hyperflexibility of a gymnast or martial artist, so never feel compelled to compete in flexibility terms. Always remember to move into each stretch slowly and smoothly, holding it for five to ten seconds at the beginning. If you are serious about improving your flexibility, try adding five seconds a week until you can hold it for about thirty seconds. Relax after each individual stretch then and repeat twice more. Stretching exercises are best done little and often. Five minutes before and after training will pay dividends. Stretching the muscle groups worked between sets can also be very beneficial. Stretching also helps get rid of stiffness after hard workouts. Try to do just ten minutes every day and you will soon feel the benefit.

Partner Stretching

A partner can often help you to improve your flexibility, but it is very important that they be sensitive to your limits. Never bounce into a stretch and never force it. If you are very stiff and have difficulty getting started with stretching routines, a partner may be just what you need as they can help place you in positions you would find difficult to reach alone. The photographs show just two of the possible ways that they can help to improve shoulder and hip and hamstring flexibility.

Partner stretching (1) and (2).

37

EXERCISE FORM

Go into almost any gym and you are likely to see two different kinds of trainer. The first is mainly concerned with lifting as much weight as possible and does not seem to care too much how he does it. These people often attract a lot of attention, lifting enormous weights and making a lot of noise to assist them in their efforts. The second type may or may not lift heavy weights, but is noticeably more concerned to do each exercise correctly, with good form.

Good form in bodybuilding means working the muscle group that the exercise is intended to work, without cheating and bringing other muscles into play. Good form means intensity, concentration and control. Movements will tend to be quite slow in the negative phase of the movement (the eccentric or lowering action in the bench press, for example) and slightly quicker and more explosive in the concentric, lifting phase. The bodybuilder who trains in good form pays attention to grip, posture, breathing and the alignment of things like stands and benches. The exercises are performed slowly and smoothly with just the right amount of weight to make the last three repetitions really hard. Good form is one of the secrets of continuous progress. How you lift is more important than how much you lift.

SCHEDULES FOR THE BEGINNER

First Month

Remember, before doing your bodybuilding exercises, to spend ten minutes stretching and warming up, using the exercises described

This schedule involves training three days a week with one exercise per body part, three sets per exercise. The first set is a warm up consisting of fifteen repetitions. It is followed by two sets of ten repetitions. Rest for about two minutes between sets and write down all your repetitions and poundages. There are two sets of exercises, group A and group B.

Bodypart	Group A	Group B
Thighs	Barbell squats	Leg press or hack
Hamstrings	Leg curls	Straight-leg deadlift
Back	Dumb-bell rows	Pull-downs
Chest	Bench press	Incline bench press
Shoulders	Press behind neck	Military press
Biceps	Barbell curls	Seated dumb-bell curls
Triceps	Triceps push-downs	Dips between benches
Abdominals	Sit-ups	Leg-raises
Calves	Standing calf-raise	Seated calf-raise

Each group contains an exercise for each of the main body parts. Training three times a week, you would do the exercises in group A on Monday and Friday and the exercises from group B on Wednesday. The following week you would do the group B exercises on Monday and Friday and the group A exercises on Wednesday. This pattern, ABABAB should be repeated throughout the month.

It is extremely important to regard the first month as a learning experience and to do your best to learn to do the exercises in perfect form. Most gymnasiums have competent instructors or experienced bodybuilders in them. Do not be afraid to ask for help or advice on how to perform an exercise if you are unsure. Use your common sense, of course. Nothing is more irritating for serious bodybuilders than to have some beginner interrupt their workouts, pestering them with questions. Choose the right moment, perhaps when they are cooling down after a workout and feeling good about how their training has gone! As you train, feel how your muscles respond and write everything down. As far as routines go, once you start a routine give it at least a month to six weeks.

Second Month

Moving into the second month, the frequency of training stays at three days a week, but we begin tailoring programmes to meet specific needs.

The three sets are still used but now the first set consists of fifteen reps done with enough weight to make the last two reps a bit of an effort, in the second set twelve reps and in the third set ten reps. The weight should be increased slightly for each set. This is the overload principle: by giving muscles a little bit more to do, they will adapt and grow bigger and stronger. The amount you can increase the weight by in a given exercise will depend to a large extent on the exercise itself and on how strong you become at it. Obviously large, powerful muscle groups like the back and legs adapt to overload more easily than small groups like the biceps. If you did ten reps with 70lb in the squat in your first workout and added just 5lb a month you would be doing ten reps with 140lb in just over a year: a 100 per cent increase in training volume and strength, well within most people's reach. If you had begun doing curls at the same time and also added 5lb a month, you would be curling nearly 100lb: an increase in training volume of over 200 per cent, which would not be a realistic target weight for the average trainer for another two years!

So the best way to proceed is to write down all your weights sets and reps and keep a record of how easy or difficult the different sets feel.

There will also be days when you feel well above and well below your normal levels of energy and strength. Avoid leaving the gym absolutely exhausted; leave a little bit in the tank so that you come back to the next workout eager and ready to improve, rather than stiff and worn out!

The overweight trainer will add more aerobic activities to workouts, doing twenty minutes of exercise bike or treadmill after the bodybuilding exercises. The ideal aerobic fat-burning effect – without muscle loss – is achieved by maintaining the pulse rate at 60 per cent of maximum. To work out what your training pulse rate should be for aerobic exercise, subtract your age from 220. (This is the estimated maximum pulse rate; in reality it can vary considerably, but without taking a special test with trained supervision an exact figure cannot be arrived at.) In the case of a twenty-year-old, the figure would be 200, for a thirty-year-old 190, a forty-year-old 180 and so on. Corresponding target training rates of 60 per cent of these figures are 120, 114 and 108. These figures are at the bottom end of the scale for an aerobic training effect, but this is the best way to burn fat without the risk of breaking down muscle tissue. Working at about 75 per cent and sustaining pulse rates of 150, 142 and 135 per minute would build fitness faster, but would cause slight muscle loss.

Third Month

During the third month, weights can be increased, but never at the expense of good form; sets and reps should be kept the same. After three months' training, more interest can be generated in workouts by increasing the variety of exercise groups from two to four and beginning to split the body into areas. These are each to be trained more intensely, rather than trying to do the whole body in a single workout. This is a 'cost-effective' way to train, as it means you get the right combination of

Group A
Chest

Pec deck	Decline dumb-bell press
Decline press	Bent arm pull-overs

Back

Bent-over rows	Deadlifts
Straight-arm pull-overs	Reverse grip pull-downs to chest

Shoulders

Seated dumb-bell press	Arnold press
Lateral raises	Bent-over lateral raises

Midsection

Incline sit-ups	Hanging leg-raises

Group B
Thighs

Front squats	Hack squats
Leg extensions	Lunges

Hamstrings

Leg curls	Straight-legged deadlift

Calves

Donkey raises	Toe presses

Biceps

E–Z bar curls	Inclined bench dumb-bell curls
Concentration curls	Reverse curls

Triceps

Dips between bars	Triceps extension with dumb-bell
Kickbacks	Prone dumb-bell extension

Group C
Chest

Dumb-bell press	Flat bench press
Inclined barbell press	Inclined dumb-bell press

Back

Pull-downs to chest	Pull-downs behind neck
Dumb-bell rows	Seated pulley rows

Shoulders

Press behind neck	Military press
Upright rows	Shrugs

Midsection

Crunches	Leg raises

Group D		
Thighs		
	Squats	Leg presses
	Leg extensions	Lunges
Hamstrings		
	Leg curls	Straight-leg deadlift
Calves		
	Standing	Seated
Biceps		
	Barbell curl	Preacher curl
	Seated dumb-bell curl	Hammer curl
Triceps		
	Triceps push-downs	Narrow grip bench press
	Lying French press	Dips between benches

exercise intensity and rest necessary to grow without having to spend too long in the gym. The chest, back, shoulders and abdominals are trained by doing one of the routines contained in group A or C. The exercises in groups B and D train the legs and arms. These workouts could be done Monday, Wednesday and Friday. This would involve training six times in every two weeks following the order ABCDAB. Excellent progress can be made in the first year by following these routines and resting and eating correctly. By writing everything down you can keep a record of your improvement and progress – or lack of it. If you are eating sufficiently but still feel tired you may need to rest more. You could train one day on, one day off, one day on two days off, one day on one day off, one day on two days off.

Monday group A. Tuesday rest. Wednesday group B. Thursday and Friday rest. Saturday group C. Sunday rest. Monday group D and so on. The beauty of writing everything down is that over a period of months you can determine what works for you and what is less effective. Strict form is essential. Only increase weight when you can do your target repetitions in strict form. Unfit beginners may need to rest as

much as three minutes between sets in the early months, but should aim to reduce the rest time by about fifteen seconds every eight weeks or so, gradually getting down to a 1½ minute rest between each set.

By following the routines outlined above, you should make good progress as long as you are consistent. Do not keep changing your routines, write everything down and eat plenty. Most people's biggest mistake is that they do not eat enough good quality food.

DIET FOR THE BEGINNER

Your diet does not need to be as strict as a competitive bodybuilder, but it has to have enough protein and carbohydrates to fuel your workouts and allow for muscle growth. Buy a food calorie-counter but look for one which tells you how many grams of protein, fat and carbohydrate you get from typical servings. Also check the glycaemic index of the foods you like. Certain foods have an extremely high glycaemic index, which means the body stores them as fat much more easily. Diet is not just a question of calorie-counting

Diet for a New Bodybuilder

Breakfast	Porridge oats (skimmed or semi-skimmed milk if necessary), four-egg cheese omelette and a piece of fruit, vitamins, tea or coffee
Mid-morning	Protein drink with skimmed milk
Lunch	Chicken breast or four thighs, jacket potatoes, green vegetables (cabbage, broccoli, spinach, etc.)
Mid-afternoon	Protein drink and a piece of fruit
Evening meal	Steak or fish, rice or pasta and mixed vegetables
Supper	Protein drink

– it is also important to know what kind of calories you are eating. There is a lot more information and opinions about diet in Chapter 5 on nutrition, but the table above is typical of what the up-and-coming bodybuilder should be eating. Water (1½–2 litres) should be drunk during the day too.

EXERCISE TECHNIQUE

Grip

The grip you take for a given exercise is one of the most important factors affecting the actual training effect achieved. Where training with a barbell is concerned, there are really only two hand positions and they are the overgrasp and the undergrasp, but there is a wide range of different spacings possible.

- The undergrasp is the standard grip taken from the anatomical reference position, the arms by the sides and the hands supinated, palms facing forwards. The grip for doing barbell curl is a typical example.
- The overgrasp is the name given to the grip

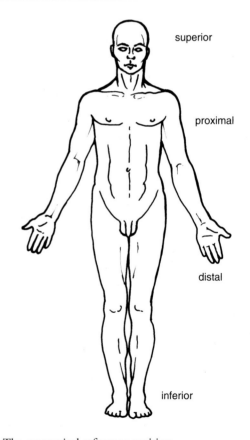

The anatomical reference position.

superior

proximal

distal

inferior

42

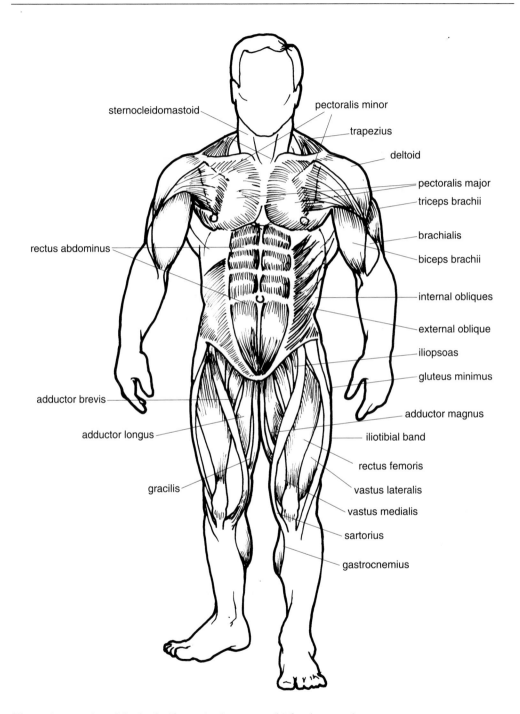

sternocleidomastoid

pectoralis minor

trapezius

deltoid

pectoralis major

triceps brachii

brachialis

rectus abdominus

biceps brachii

internal obliques

external oblique

iliopsoas

gluteus minimus

adductor brevis

adductor magnus

adductor longus

iliotibial band

rectus femoris

vastus lateralis

gracilis

vastus medialis

sartorius

gastrocnemius

The major muscles of the body (front view); *see* page 54 for the rear view.

Overgrasp grip.

Posture

Posture is very important when lifting weights. Maintaining the correct posture is the best way to avoid injuries. Correct posture involves knowing which muscle groups you are supposed to be working when you perform a given exercise and carrying out the exercise in perfect form. For any exercise where a weight is supported standing up, the back ought to be as straight as possible. When training legs, doing squats for example, remember to bend the legs at the hips and knees, not at the waist. Any kind of pulling movement should be done keeping the trunk upright and straight. Pressing movements done seated or lying flat should always be performed with the back flat against the padded bench. An arched lower back is an important aspect of powerlifting technique, when doing pressing movements. The bodybuilder does not need to take risks, however, as the aim is not to demonstrate strength by lifting maximum weights, but to isolate individual muscle groups and work them intensely so as to stimulate maximum possible muscle growth.

taken with the hands pronated. This involves facing the bar and turning the hands so that the palms face to the rear as when doing Olympic-style weightlifting or pressing movements.

- The mixed grip involves holding with one hand undergrasp and the other overgrasp. It is normally only used for deadlifting where very heavy weights are being handled to stop the bar rolling in the hands and causing the fingers to open.

Spacing is crucially important in a number of exercises as it determines which muscles work hardest doing certain exercises In the bench press for instance a wide grip means you keep the elbows directly under the bar and the pectorals are fully engaged and work hard. A narrow grip allows the elbows to come in to the sides of the body and works the triceps more directly.

Feet Position

Generally, with most standing exercises, the feet should be shoulder-width apart and parallel. This is the most stable, balanced position for the majority of exercises. The toes normally point forwards. There is a certain amount of variety where leg exercises are concerned, and indeed changing the angulation of the feet often changes the effect of the exercise, throwing the stresses onto different muscles. Try squatting or leg pressing with the feet parallel, shoulder-width apart and toes pointing forwards. Try another set, but change the feet position; let the heels almost touch and angle the feet at 45 degrees and feel the difference in the movement and how different muscle groups come into play in each case. Try the same experiment with leg extensions and leg curls, turning the feet inwards and outwards on successive sets, and you will feel the difference.

The first time you make these sort of adjustments be careful not to use too much weight and perform the exercises very slowly.

With exercises where you are prone or seated, the feet are generally shoulder-width apart. The important thing is that you should feel stable and on balance during the exercise. Poor form on a seated dumb-bell press could easily cause you to lean to one side, and if the feet were too close together, you would lose your balance and be unable to recover it.

Factors Affecting Strength

While there certainly are some very strong bodybuilders – Franco Columbo was, pound for pound, one of the strongest men in the world by any kind of reckoning – it is also clear that the biggest muscles is not always necessarily the strongest. Muscle strength and size are related – generally, a bigger muscle is a stronger muscle, but there are many other more important factors affecting the development and demonstration of strength capacity.

Strength is determined by a number of physiological factors. Genetically predetermined bone lengths and muscle-attachment points can make for considerable differences in leverage. Another important factor is the force–velocity relationship, the speed at which a muscle lengthens or shortens. This is determined by skill factors and the distribution of red and white twitch muscle fibres, the white fibres being the ones that provide explosive power, while the red ones determine strength endurance. Equally important is the muscle's length at any given point in its range of motion – known as the length–tension relationship – which varies according to the changing degrees of overlap between the thick and thin molecular filaments of which all muscle fibres are composed.

Other more fluctuating variables such as energy levels, sleep patterns, dietary changes, alcohol or drug abuse, work stresses, illness and age must also be taken into consideration. Seasonal variation too makes a difference. In cold climates, people tend to eat more in the winter which usually means it is a good time to make strength gains. The opposite is true of hot very climates where summer sees people inclined to eat less, not sleep so well and generally have lower energy levels.

Finally, as with all physical or athletic performances, psychological factors are vitally important to the final result. In order to lift a maximum weight you have to want to and you have to believe that you can. Different people are more or less motivated by different situations: medals, records, taking the task seriously, a need for a sense of personal achievement, the need to display physical superiority and the desire to impress others are just some of the motivating factors that can, and do, affect performance.

As with developing your physique, developing your strength levels is something that you should undertake in competition with yourself. Friendly competition with training partners and friends in the gym is healthy and can be good for motivation, but if your aim is just to have a good-looking aesthetically pleasing muscular body, there is no need to become obsessed by how much you can lift. Remember: how you lift is more important than how much!

EQUIPMENT

Free Weights and Machines

In the bodybuilding world, there have been numerous fierce debates about the relative merits of free weights versus machines. This debate began with the introduction of the Universal range of exercise machines, which resemble the multiple station multigym and polygyms so popular in sport centres and the YMCA in Great Britain. There are numerous advantages to using such machines, but disadvantages as well. The debate grew much more heated as a result of the aggressive marketing tactics employed by Arthur Jones who pioneered the Nautilus system and range of equipment. He claimed that his Nautilus system was the most effective training system ever devised and that it had rendered free weights obsolete at a stroke. Bodybuilders and athletes have argued among themselves over a number of years about the truth of these claims and the relative strengths and weaknesses of both systems.

What eventually became clear (and really ought to have been obvious from the beginning) is that there is nothing to stop the individual selecting those exercises, pieces of apparatus, or training methods, in an eclectic way. The modern consensus is that the intelligent approach is to try things out, find out what works best for you, and keep doing it while discarding what does not. Most well-equipped gymnasiums will offer a range of equipment including barbells, dumb-bells, Olympic bars and various machines. Some gym owners may buy in a particular line of equipment because they want a designer gym with a coherent colour scheme and can often get a better financial deal by buying from a sole supplier. Some of the very best gyms, however, usually owned by experienced bodybuilders, ex-champion athletes or physical trainers are totally eclectic and have individual machines from a variety of manufacturers, each one selected because the owner feels that it is the best machine of its kind available for doing a particular job. The inexperienced trainer, of course, has little or no idea what the best machine for a particular exercise is, having had no opportunity to try them all out; in fact, individual differences like limb length and height are important factors. Most machines are designed for people of average height, but a leg press designed for the average man is likely to be far from ideal for a 6ft 10in (210cm) basketball player or a 5ft (150cm) Olympic lifter. These are, of course, extreme cases, but initially it is worth trying out a few different gyms before deciding which one to join.

Something that should be understood right from the outset is that if you train regularly on one kind of equipment, you become familiar with it and used to it, and it begins to feel right or normal to you. Changing gyms and using different equipment often gives you something of a shock, strength levels seem to fluctuate and certain exercises do not feel right. It is usually just a passing phase and a matter of giving yourself time to get used to the different equipment. There is also a school of thought that advocates regular changes of this kind to stop the body becoming complacent and getting used to the same exercises and to intensify the exercise effect by emphasizing the differences.

Using Variable-resistance Machines

Not all machine-based training systems work in the same way: there is a huge difference between the simple multigym design and the cambered Nautilus and Cybex equipment. There are over twenty-five different Nautilus exercise stations and each one usually permits some two or three exercises to be performed, in total some forty or fifty different exercises. Unlike a barbell curl, where the muscle works at a different intensity depending upon the amount of leverage available, the variable-resistance system ensures maximum stimulation of the muscles throughout the complete range of movement. The following principles normally apply when using variable-resistance equipment.

1. Perform eight to twelve repetitions with a complete range of movement. If you cannot do eight repetitions, decrease the weight by 5 per cent. If you can do more than twelve increase the weight by 5 per cent.

2. The number of repetitions performed should take the given muscle group to failure.
3. Train large muscle groups first and small muscle groups last, e.g. thighs, back, chest, abdominals, shoulders, arms, calves.
4. The speed of movement must be slow. Each repetition should take from 4 to 5 seconds, 1½ to 2 seconds for the concentric phase of the movement (lifting the weight) and 2½ to 3½ seconds for the eccentric phase (lowering the weight).
5. Ensure a full range of movement and a maximum muscle stretch at the final phase of the eccentric movement.

The implications of these principles gave rise to the high-intensity type training system championed by the remarkable Mike Mentzer in the 1970s and 1980s. Considered revolutionary at the time as well as highly contentious, the system still has its advocates. One of the most controversial ideas for many experienced bodybuilders was that a single set would be sufficient to stimulate muscle growth. However, it has been demonstrated that if the intensity and subsequent recuperation are sufficient, growth will take place. Some exercise physiologists maintain that athletes other than bodybuilders, such as gymnasts, wrestlers, judo players and those sportsmen who want to develop tensile strength are those who have the most to gain from training with Nautilus-type equipment, free weights being preferred for developing strength for ballistic sports like athletics, field events and football.

Machines are not the panacea for rapid muscular development that their manufacturers often claim; they have many good points but there are also certain disadvantages. Some machines exercise certain muscle groups in isolation more effectively than free weights, but they are incomplete and unsatisfactory as a total exercise system for a number of reasons. Training with free weights develops coordination skills and balance, you learn to use the body as a whole, synergistically, so as to control the weight. Ligaments, tendons and connective tissue are brought into play and strengthened, and joint stability improved more by using free weights than machines. The process of training to failure on every set is also extremely difficult to keep up, psychologically as well as physically, and only the most highly motivated trainees are capable of sustaining the effort necessary to continue to make progress over a long period of time. A final reason that explains why free weights remain more popular than machines is that lifting barbells and dumb-bells is a form of strength display more easily identified with by the man in the street. This simple ego gratification may not be a very good scientific reason for preferring one system to another, but at the end of the day, it is one of the main reasons that people keep going to gyms and working out.

CHECKING PROGRESS

It is no exaggeration to say that the bodybuilder's best friend can be a detailed, well-kept training diary. For beginners it is a useful tool to help remember what exercises they have to do, in what order, as well as sets and repetitions to be performed. Beginners will tend to write down what they have to do then follow the plan, modifying either the poundages or the repetitions and sets, depending upon how realistic their expectations were in the first place. More advanced trainees who like to train instinctively will write up what they have done as they do the exercises. If you keep a detailed training diary, containing details of diet as well as workouts, it can be doubly helpful as you can use the information intelligently and experiment with routines, nutrition and supplementation to find out which combinations work best for you.

Mirrors

The aspiring bodybuilder has three basic tools that can be used to check progress: the mirror, the tape measure and the scale. Of these three, the mirror is probably the easiest to use and the most important. Most of us know when we look bigger, leaner, better defined, more muscular, more bloated, or fatter. What you see when you look at yourself in a mirror is, however, affected by numerous other factors, including current levels of self-esteem and self-satisfaction, so objectivity can vary considerably from week to week. Arnold Schwarzenegger once advised trainees to look at themselves with a paper bag over their heads as an aid to being totally objective about their bodies. The thinking behind this seemingly outrageous piece of advice (Arnold always had a reputation for being a bit of natural comedian and practical joker) is that most of us are complacent about our bodies and tend to see what we want to see when we look at ourselves in the mirror. When you don't see your face it is easier to look at your body as if it were someone else's and consequently it becomes easier to identify faults and weak points.

Photography

Another useful aid to checking your progress that can help keep you motivated and inspired is photography. Most people have a spare camera lying around that does not get used for very much except at holiday times. A roll of film can contain twenty-four or thirty-six exposures so it is possible to do two or three shots per week over eight or twelve weeks to monitor and keep a record of your progress. By shooting three rolls of thirty-six exposures you can have a permanent record of your progress during a whole year. A good tip to avoid optical inconsistencies is to shoot the same poses from the same distance with the same lens in the same lighting. Lighting, in particular, can make a huge difference to a bodybuilder's apparent muscularity and size, depending upon whether it is frontal, side or overhead and whether it is daylight, tungsten or flash. Some cameras have databacks which will imprint the date on the corner of the negative so that there is no danger of getting confused about which shots were taken when. The same is true of the video camera which has the added advantages of being instant and there being no development costs involved.

Video

Some people find that videotaping their workouts is an extremely useful exercise as it allows them to see how they train, which exercises they perform correctly and in strict form and which ones they tend to be a little sloppy in. Video review is an extremely useful tool for improving exercise technique and for allowing us to make objective appraisals of how our bodies actually look.

A professional production is not necessary: a competent friend, girlfriend, wife or other member of the family can tape the workout, ideally without distracting or interfering, so that it is as close to being a normal workout as possible. Of course, you should ask for permission, explaining what you want to do beforehand and be sure not to be a nuisance to other people who are training there. It would be excessive to tape every workout, but once in a while it can be a useful exercise and watching workout tapes may help to add interest and enthusiasm when the going gets tough. If you make a tape every three months, over a period of time you will be able to build up an interesting visual record of your progress. If you have corresponding training diaries containing a record of training and dietary details, they should help keep you on the right track and serve as a reference if ever you begin training other people.

3 Training: Further Principles

INTRODUCTION

The amount of time that must be spent training so as to be able to go in for a contest varies enormously from individual to individual and depends on all sorts of factors, such as a good genetic potential, persistence, motivation and adequate nutrition. Someone with good genetics might be ready for a first show in two or three years, the less gifted may take three times as long to get into reasonable condition.

CYCLING AND PERIODIZATION

Bodybuilding for competition inevitably involves a certain amount of periodization or cycling of training in order to be able to come in in top form on the day of a given event. Competitive bodybuilders aiming to win one major title a year tend to follow a macro-cycle of eight to nine months in which they eat and train for mass, muscular growth and increases in size and strength, and three to four months in which they concentrate on chiselling the physique, hardening up and getting rid of all excess fat. Training for size involves doing certain basic exercises slowly and in strict form with the aim being to overload the muscles by gradually increasing the weight in each set. The final set should involve maximum effort and concentration with the most weight that can be handled in good form in order to fully stimulate muscle growth.

During this pre-competitive phase, it is vital for the bodybuilder to consume large amounts of carbohydrates and proteins to fuel workouts and ensure muscle recovery and growth. Three months before the competition date the typical bodybuilder will usually be from 4 to 5kg heavier than his ideal competitive weight. In the last three months training and diet are modified to get rid of the extra unwanted body fat, while retaining muscle size and density to guarantee a massive, highly defined look on the day of the contest. The pace of training sessions usually quickens in this phase; the repetitions performed per set are increased and the rest time between sets reduced along with the amount of weight being handled.

Increasingly, among the more serious competitive bodybuilders, especially in the professional sport where there is big money to be earned, the macro-cycle described above tends to be modified, or broken down into a number of mini-cycles. If a bodybuilder wants to compete twice a year, the cycle is modified so that it contains two blocks of four to four-and-a-half months in which the emphasis is on building size, each followed by a six- to eight-week pre-competitive phase where the aim is to get defined. If the aim is to compete three times a year, the first phase is a relatively long four month period of training for size followed by just a month of pre-competition training for definition, the second phase involves two-and-a-half months' training for size and six weeks of training for definition. The final phase is split into two six-week blocks, the first six weeks going for size and the final six weeks for definition.

The two-cycle phasing of the macro-cycle is thus repeated three times within the course of the year. This has many advantages for intermediate and advanced bodybuilders. The main advantage is that of getting to know how your body responds to changes in diet and training. The bodybuilder can also avoid the tendency to get very heavy by bulking up too far, an error many fall into when they let their diet get out of hand. Once you gain fat beyond a certain level, it becomes increasingly difficult to lose it again. It also gives the bodybuilder the opportunity to compete more often and thereby gain more experience of the whole process of competition – strong points, what can go wrong, how to avoid mistakes the next time around. Many learn as much about the psychological aspects of preparing themselves for contest as they do about the purely physical.

RECUPERATION

Bodybuilding is not just weight training. One of the fundamental parts of the bodybuilding process is recuperation. After an intense workout muscle tissue is broken down and requires rest and adequate nutrition in order to be replenished. Recovery is rebuilding. Training is about breaking down muscles, resting and eating are what enable muscle growth to take place.

Beginners tend to start out training three times a week, usually Mondays, Wednesdays and Fridays so that they have a full 48 hours' recovery between training sessions. Many people actually make some of their best gains on this kind of programme because they get the balance between intensity and recovery just right. However, it is true that the body, while thriving on routine also adapts to it, so it becomes increasingly necessary to change routines in order to keep making progress.

A normal strategy for people who have trained for a year or two is to switch to working out four times per week doing two or three muscle groups (sometimes referred to as 'bodyparts') per workout. On a four-day-a-week programme, the entire body can be thoroughly trained and each muscle group gets a full 48 hours to recover. A standard structure for training the different body parts is as follows:

Week 1   Monday and Thursday
Chest, shoulders, arms
Tuesday and Friday
Legs and back

Week 2   Monday and Thursday
Legs and back
Tuesday and Friday
Chest, shoulders, arms

By changing the days every other week, the muscle groups do not rest more than the optimum 48 hours (if the days were not alternated then there would be times when the rest period extended to 72 hours).

When four days per week training ceases to be effective the training load can be increased to five days per week, so gaining an extra workout.

Week 1   Monday, Wednesday and Friday
Chest, shoulders, arms
Tuesday and Thursday
Legs and back

Week 2   Monday, Wednesday and Friday
Legs and back
Tuesday and Thursday
Chest, shoulders, arms

Weekends should be spent allowing the body to recover and resting. This does not mean lying around and doing nothing. Rest refers to a break from the kind of high intensity, catabolic training you have been doing in the gym. Rest should be active; remember anything that speeds up the metabolism helps to burn fat and promotes definition. Walking, dancing, riding a bicycle, the occasional swim or a short jog or playing some sort of sport for fun are recommended. It is not a good idea to overdo physical activities. Do not take up anything too serious, as it will be likely to sap your energy for your bodybuilding efforts. Something that requires coordination, like a friendly game of table tennis or volleyball, rather than a very physically demanding sport like rugby, soccer or judo is probably a better option.

More advanced trainers can increase their training frequency to six days a week. By doing this, each muscle group can be trained three times per week.

Monday and Thursday	Chest and back
Tuesday and Friday	Shoulders and arms
Wednesday and Saturday	Legs and abdominals

Pre-competition training six times per week is more differentiated:

Monday and Thursday	Biceps, triceps, shoulders and forearms
Tuesday and Friday	Chest, back and abdominals
Wednesday and Saturday	Legs and lower back

It should be pointed out that not all muscle groups respond to training at the same rate. The abdominals, calves and forearms are particularly problematic to develop for many people. Many high-level bodybuilders do additional training sessions for just those body parts, often as a separate supplementary routine early in the morning or at lunch-time. Serious bodybuilders do a lot of training and because of the overloads and high intensity involved, many find it more useful to split their training loads into two daily sessions with a six- to eight-hour gap between them. This is known as the 'double-split' system or principle.

UNDERSTANDING EXERCISE BIOMECHANICS

Knowing how often to train is not as obvious as some people like to think it is. More is not always better and it is worth experimenting with different training patterns to see how you respond. This experimentation is particularly vital if you do not have an experienced trainer or someone guiding you. Always write everything down: workout details, frequency, rest times, diet details, drinking habits – anything you can think of that might affect your progress.

Anyone who has ever been in a gym will have heard people talking about 'aerobics' and 'anaerobic training', 'good exercise form', 'loose form' and 'cheating'. These are just a few of the terms popularly used in bodybuilding jargon and exercise physiology. This jargon rolls off the tongue with practised ease in many cases, but it is really important to know what it means as it is frequently misused and misunderstood by large sections of the population.

The question of exercise form is one of the most important. 'Form' refers to the way in which you do your exercises which is of vital importance for avoiding injury and making progress. There are certain biomechanical factors that should be consciously studied and understood by anyone taking up an exercise programme or starting to do a new exercise movement.

ANATOMY, KINESIOLOGY AND EXERCISE PHYSIOLOGY

Anatomy is the study of the body, its physical composition and structure. Doctors study anatomy to learn about how the body works and to understand the brain, central nervous system, circulatory and respiratory systems, digestion, excretion, the functions and locations of the higher organs, veins, arteries, blood vessels, muscles, ligaments, tendons, bones and a plethora of other facts of fundamental biological importance. It is not necessary to be a doctor, or study to the extent that they do – just so that you can do and enjoy physical training and bodybuilding. It is in your own interests to be as well informed as possible. The more information you have about a subject, the better your position to make an informed decision. Being well informed does not just mean reading the monthly bodybuilding magazines and studying the catalogues of bodybuilding products they contain. It means understanding certain basic facts about exercise, nutrition, recuperation, anatomy and kinesiology. One of the major problems with many magazine articles is that they often contain conflicting information, apparently contradicting each other.

Kinesiology is the study of movement – of the body's biomechanical functions and systems of locomotion. It covers any kind of movement from apparently simple acts of crawling, walking, running, swimming, jumping and lifting to more complex learned skills like throwing, wrestling, boxing, dancing and gymnastics. Many sports scientists utilize kinesiological methods and techniques to assist athletes in speeding up the acquisition of movement skills and refining their technique.

The body is a remarkable combination of muscles, bones, nerves, ligaments, tendons, cartilages and joints which function synergistically to allow movement to be possible. Certain internal movements are crucial to normal bodily functioning, such as the beating of the heart, the blinking of the eyes, digestion and breathing and these are described as 'involuntary', in the sense that you do not need to think about them or will them to happen in order for them to take place. 'Voluntary' movements are made by making a conscious decision to do so. They enlist the mechanical energy stored in the body's chemical systems to activate muscles which attach via ligaments and tendons, sinews and leaders, to the bones, cartilages and joints of the skeleton to cause movement to happen.

All exercise is based on movement and bodybuilding, which employs a variety of weight-lifting exercises to stimulate muscular development, is no exception. If you understand how the various muscles, joints and bones interact in order to perform exercise movements, you will have a much better idea of exactly what is happening when you train a muscle group and how to intelligently select exercises to stimulate those muscles that you wish to train, according to the priorities you choose to establish. In Chapter 4 the pertinent kinesiological elements of the various bodybuilding exercises are described in detail. One of the aims here is to explain some of the standard terminology used in kinesiology, and frequently bandied about and misused in gymnasiums, so as to make the whole area more accessible to the layman.

The basic reference position in kinesiology is known as the 'standard anatomical reference position'. This involves standing with the feet together and arms hanging by the sides, with the hands turned out so that the palms are facing forwards. This is the preferred starting position for many physical examinations as carried out by physiotherapists, chiropractors and osteopaths. The front segments of the body are referred to as the 'anterior surface', for example the chest, abdomen and thighs, while the rear body surfaces are said to be 'posterior', the back and hamstrings, for example. The term 'lateral' is used to designate body surfaces facing away from the body's midline while medial refers to those which face towards it. So the medial ligament of the knee is the ligament on the inside of the knee, the anterior deltoid is the front deltoid, and so on.

From the anatomical reference position, the various movements that the body is capable of are described by a number of technical terms, the most important of which are the following.

'Flexion' is a term which describes any forward or backward movement of a body part, such as an arm or leg, away from the standard reference position. Raising the right arm in front of you as when doing a frontal dumb-bell raise is an example of flexion. Taking the limb back to its original position, travelling along the same movement path is called 'extension'.

If the extension movement is continued beyond the anatomical reference position the moving joint is said to 'hyperextend'. Hyperextension occurs in any movement where the back is arched, for example. The spine and neck are capable of a considerable range of movement in terms of hyperextension; ball-and-socket joints, like the hip and shoulder while offering much greater general mobility, are less capable of hyperextension and shoulders in particular may be prone to dislocation if hyperextended. Hinge joints like the knees and elbows are not normally capable of hyperextension without injury, which is the principle behind the straight arm locks in judo and other martial arts. As well as forward and backward movements, the body is capable of performing sideways or lateral movements.

From the anatomical reference position lifting a leg up to the side is known as 'abduction', because the joint opens to allow the limb to move away from the body. Abduction of the lower limb is controlled by the gluteus medius and gluteus minimus muscle groups. Abduction takes place when you sit on the floor and open your legs, when hurdling and performing similar actions. The action of adduction involves returning the limb along the same movement path to the anatomical reference position, and closing the legs which is controlled by the adductor longus, brevis and magnus. Hip and shoulder joints permit large ranges of motion in terms of abduction, but again the elbows and knees do not, and injury can easily result from abductive stresses being placed on these joints.

Other types of movements are also possible. Of particular relevance to bodybuilders trying to develop biceps and shoulders is the capacity for 'pronation' and 'supination' of the hand due to the arrangement of bones and muscles in the forearms and shoulders. The hand is said to be supinated when it is in the standard anatomical reference position; twisting the lower arm so that the palms face backwards and the knuckles are to the front is called pronation. 'Lateral flexion' occurs when the body or trunk bends sideways, the neck can rotate to the left or right and the hip and shoulder joints are capable of medial (inwards) or lateral (outwards) rotation.

Muscle Function and Arrangement

The muscular construction of the body is incredibly complex and a detailed study of how each and every one interacts is beyond the scope of a book on bodybuilding. For the bodybuilder's purposes, the important thing is to understand which muscles come into play in order to make particular movements and so gain a clear understanding of which exercises to use to stimulate growth in specific muscle groups. This is also an important consideration when deciding on schedules in order to ensure that there is sufficient recovery time built in. For example, you may be an intermediate bodybuilder who has been advised that your biceps would grow most effectively by training

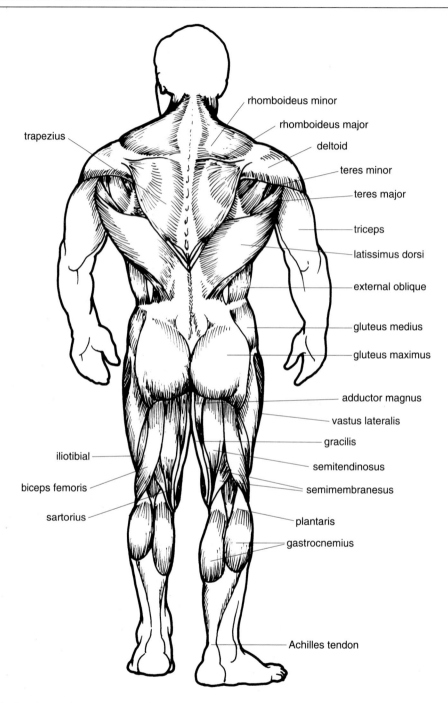

Muscle function and arrangement – the major muscles of the body (rear view); *see* page 43 for the front view.

them intensely just twice a week, on Mondays and Thursdays. No problem there except you have also been told that close-grip pull-downs are really good for thickening the upper back, which you do on Tuesdays and Fridays. Close-grip pull-downs are more of a back exercise than a biceps exercise; however, heavy poundages will result in quite an intense training effect on the biceps too. As a result, instead of training biceps twice a week you are training them four times a week – or to be more accurate, you are overtraining them. What are the implications for your schedule? Simply to do upper back and biceps in the same workout or as a double split to ensure adequate recuperation.

It should be understood that the muscles do not completely relax at any time (except under deep anaesthetic), but are in a state of permanent slight contraction called 'tonus', from which we get the terms 'muscle tone' and the expression 'to tone up'. Trained individuals naturally have better muscle tone than the untrained.

The form of a muscle is determined by the arrangement of its fibres, which is in turn dependent upon its function. There are fusiform, strap-like, triangular, quadrilateral, unipennate, bipennate and multipennate arrangements. Muscles usually attach to bone or cartilage although they also attach to ligaments or skin in some cases. Some muscles attach directly or by sinews or leaders, but most have a tendon at one or both ends. Tendons are very strong; the Achilles tendon at the back of the ankle can support up to half a ton per square inch. Tendons contain specialized nerve end-

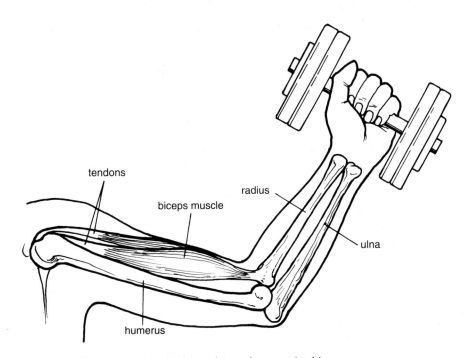

Muscles are generally connected to the bones by tendons – as in this illustration of the arm. The muscle directly responsible for making a movement is called the prime mover – in this case, bending the arms, the biceps.

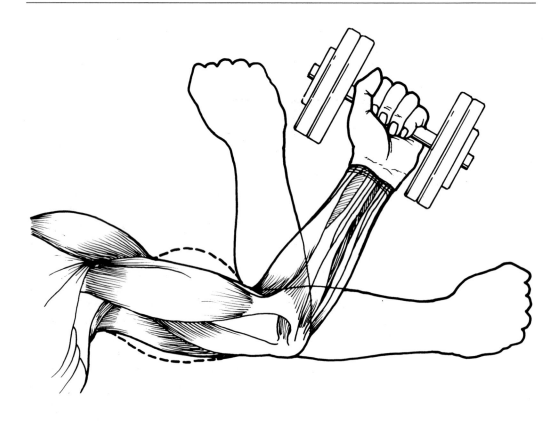

Antagonistic muscle groups function in pairs. The biceps contracts to bend the arm, the triceps contracts to straighten it.

ings that reflexively inhibit overcontraction of the muscle. When a muscle contracts, one attachment, which is called the 'origin', remains fixed; the other attachment, known as the 'insertion' moves towards it. A muscle may have two (biceps) or even three (triceps) heads of origin, but its insertion is almost always single.

Prime Movers

The 'prime mover' is the muscle directly responsible for any given movement. In the barbell curl, the biceps are the prime movers.

The 'antagonist' is the muscle capable of causing the opposite motion. When a prime mover contracts, its antagonist has to relax and pay out the necessary slack to allow the movement to take place. When the biceps contract to bend the arm, the antagonistic muscle group is the triceps which has to lengthen to permit the movement to take place.

In order for movement to take place, other muscles function as fixators which stabilize the base or fulcrum against which the prime mover acts. The head of the humerus, for instance, is unstable in the shoulder joint and when the curl is being performed, the deltoids and rotator cuff muscles come into to stabilize the shoulder joint and support the weight when the arms are straightened. Similarly, the forearm muscles must work isometrically to stabilize the wrist joints as the weight is lifted.

Muscles function as synergists by controlling intermediate joints so that prime movers can act with maximal efficiency. The same muscle can work as a prime mover, synergist or fixator, depending upon the movement being performed and the technique used. In a strict curl where only the elbow joint moves, the biceps are the prime movers. They are effectively isolated and do almost all the work of moving the weight. When a 'cheating technique' is employed, the biceps cease to be the prime movers for much of the exercise and function synergistically, adding to the greater force being generated by the legs and back to get the weight moving. (Much heavier weights can be handled by employing a cheating technique, but the biceps will not be stimulated as directly or intensely, since the legs, hips and back generate the lifting power. Olympic weightlifting is all about synergy, getting all of the muscles coordinating to lift the heaviest possible weights through highly developed technique and motor coordination skills.)

The Role of the Nervous System in Bodybuilding

All conscious movement is controlled by the central nervous system and every movement we make is a learned skill. The nervous system plays a crucial role in generating muscle tension. Every single muscle group is made up of fibres. In large muscle groups, there are literally thousands of them. The nervous system controls the tension generated by the muscle as it contracts. This is achieved by grouping bundles of muscle fibres into motor units. Each motor unit consists of a motor nerve cell which is located in the spinal cord and a predetermined number of muscle fibres, depending upon the task which the muscles are designed to carry out. All the fibres in a particular motor unit are of the same type (fast twitch or slow twitch) and are controlled by a single nerve cell. When the external demands on a muscle to generate more tension are increased the nervous system seems to enlist more and more motor units to satisfy the demands placed upon the muscle.

In the majority of situations where an increasingly heavier weight is lifted, it is believed that the nervous system automatically utilizes a size-biased recruitment system. This means that it calls initially on the smaller units controlling slow twitch fibres to make the contraction, but as the demand is increased, larger motor units controlling fast-twitch fibres are brought into play. It is believed that there are certain built-in inhibitory factors to prevent over-recruitment of motor units, since simultaneous use of all the motor units could lead to damage, although there have been cases of people in highly aroused emotional states performing incredible feats of strength – like the normal, untrained eight-stone woman who lifted a car to free her trapped daughter in an emergency. Adrenaline alters strength levels considerably and there have also been cases of individuals on drugs, PCP in particular, performing incredible feats of strength. Motor units can also increase the rate at which they transmit the electrochemical signals which trigger muscular contraction. Sometimes referred to as the 'firing rate', it can make a considerable difference in the amount of muscular tension being generated. If the rate increases from twenty-five to fifty times a second, the tension generated increases substantially. Likewise, if the firing rate increase is triggered in more motor units simultaneously, tension increases still more. One of the implications of this is that strength increases are not always linked to muscular growth, but to increased skill factors. Power-based movements like the power clean and snatch in Olympic lifting, which are performed at fast speeds, develop whole-body power not only because the whole body is enlisted in performing the movement, but because they also contain a considerable skill factor compared to the squat and bench press. This means that training in those sorts of lifts, while guaranteed to make you more powerful and stronger, will not necessarily lead to the required hypertrophy needed to make muscles bigger.

Bearing in mind that these exercises are potentially dangerous if correct exercise technique is not learned and that they require considerable flexibility and coordination, it is arguable whether they are of much use to the bodybuilder. Some bodybuilders regard them as counterproductive as they require considerable time to learn and increase the potential for injury. In the case of Olympic lifters who turn to bodybuilding, it may of course be a very different story. The same applies to the trainee who likes to play sports and wants to develop explosive power and coordination as well as an impressive physique, so it is an individual decision. In any case if you decide to include exercises like the power clean or snatch in your training programmes, find a competent instructor and learn the correct lifting technique.

There is no doubt that some people perform bodybuilding exercises much better than others. Why? Quite simply because they take the time to learn correct technique and concentrate fully on every repetition. Having in your mind's eye a picture of which muscles do what when you perform an exercise is a great aid to visualization and concentration. This in turn assists the central nervous system to learn the required skill. The mirror is a useful reference because to a certain extent you can see which muscles are working, but it is just as important to feel the movement and understand it from within. This kind of inner awareness of how your muscles, bones and joints are interacting is called 'proprioception' and can be developed by concentrating on the movements involved in the different exercises as you perform them.

Muscles function in many different ways depending on the nature of the exercise they are involved in performing. Some work as prime movers, a term which, as already explained, designates the muscle group of primary importance in performing a given movement, but other muscles also come into play as synergists or stabilizers. In bench press, for example, the prime mover is the pectoralis major, but the deltoids and triceps work as synergists, and the biceps, and upper back muscles come into play as stabilizers.

The easiest thing to grasp in an exercise is which muscles are the prime movers in a given movement. However, although the prime movers tend to do the most work, they do not always give out first especially when they are large muscle groups. Sometimes therefore it is necessary to pre-exhaust a muscle group to focus the intensity more effectively.

How Muscles Work

Muscles are only capable of contracting and so, in order for a muscle to lengthen after making a contraction, it requires either gravity or a partner muscle to contract to restore it to its original length. These paired groups of muscle which act upon one another are called 'antagonistic pairs'. The triceps and biceps of the upper arm form an antagonistic pair. The triceps straightens the arm (extension) while the biceps bends it (flexion). Despite only being capable of contraction, muscles can generate force whether shortening or being lengthened. A consequence of this is that there are two different types of contraction that take place in muscles. When a muscle shortens, such as when the biceps contract to curl a dumb-bell, the contraction is described as a 'concentric contraction'. However, in the descent phase of the same exercise, when the barbell is lowered under control, even though the biceps lengthen they remain under tension. This type of contraction, where force is generated by the muscle as it lengthens, is called an 'eccentric contraction'. Eccentric contractions performed slowly are particularly effective for building strength and many bodybuilders and powerlifters perform partner-assisted negative-only repetitions with weights heavier than what they can lift unassisted, precisely for that reason.

Understanding the relationship between antagonistic pairs of muscles is also important for learning to stretch muscles safely and effectively, to promote suppleness and prevent the body from developing the muscle-bound look.

Muscle Fibres

The skeletal muscles that the bodybuilder sets out to develop are made up of individual cells called fibres. These fibres fall into two distinct categories, determined by the speed at which they can contract: 'fast twitch' and 'slow twitch'. The fast-twitch fibres are white and the slow-twitch type are red. Slow-twitch fibres are important for endurance because they do not fatigue as quickly as fast-twitch fibre. Fast-twitch fibres are also divided into types A and B which have some different properties from one another. Type A fast-twitch fibres generate a greater maximum tension at a faster rate, but tire more quickly. Type B fast-twitch fibres generate less tension but tire less quickly than type A.

The distribution of fast- and slow-twitch fibres varies from individual to individual and also within different muscle groups. The differing proportions of red and white fibres tend to condition athletic performance to a large extent. Events which depend on pure speed and explosive power, like sprinting or weightlifting, are dominated by athletes with high concentrations of white, fast-twitch muscle fibres. Individuals who have higher proportions of slow, red twitch muscle fibres are better suited to pure endurance events, like long-distance running, swimming and triathlon. Certain types of fast-twitch fibres will adapt to the kind of training undertaken and are said to turn pink as they adapt from their normal state to the demands placed on them by the training stimulus.

FITNESS CONSIDERATIONS

Aerobic and Anaerobic Exercise

The body generates energy for movement and exercise purposes using two main systems. 'Aerobic exercise' is the name given to physical activity which is of low intensity and longer duration and which utilizes oxygen to generate energy. Aerobic exercises stimulate the body's oxidative metabolism and use oxygen to burn stored fat. When 'anaerobic exercise' is performed, the energy is supplied from blood sugar and results in the production of lactic acid – the substance that causes the burning feeling in the muscle on the last few repetitions of a hard set, and also feelings of stiff muscles after training. The instantly available energy that powers the anaerobic system is supplied by breaking down adenosine triphosphate (ATP) which is the fuel for all energy requiring processes in cells. ATP is stored in both red and white muscle fibres, and gets broken into adenosine diphosphate (ADP) in order for energy to be produced. Both systems are interactive and interdependent, and work simultaneously all the time, to a greater or lesser extent, to produce the ATP demanded by particular stimuli. Slow-twitch fibres work aerobically whereas fast-twitch fibres work anaerobically.

Anaerobic fitness is determined by the body's capacity to tolerate lactic acid production. The sprinting events such as the 100m, 200m and 400m are good tests of anaerobic capacity. The 400m, in particular, where a maximum effort has to made and sustained generates maximum lactic acid production which causes extreme local muscular fatigue. A similar effect is achieved by doing sets of heavy squats or power cleans. In the initial stages of any exercise both systems are engaged and the aerobic energy production system only becomes fully activated after about seven minutes of low-intensity exercise. At this point it becomes a steady-state exercise. 'Steady state' refers to the steady production and elimination of lactic acid as exercise takes place. Typical examples of steady-state exercises are even-paced cycling, swimming, skipping, rowing, jogging and walking. In the initial stages of such submaximal exercise, the energy supplies are met by glycogen stored in the muscles, blood glucose and then plasma free fatty acids and intramuscular fats. In typical weight-training circuits, the effect is more likely to be anaerobic rather than aerobic as a given muscle has to be exercised for more than two minutes before the aerobic energy system kicks in.

Many sports require participants to develop both power and endurance so it is important to devise training regimes that develop both kinds of fibres and train both the anaerobic and aerobic systems in proportion to the demands of the activity. To appear in a bodybuilding show does not require great aerobic fitness, but the anaerobic demands of competitive posing can be surprisingly high depending on how skilled you are at posing.

Aerobic training in order to improve cardiovascular fitness and not just to burn fat should be a part of the bodybuilder's training regime simply from the common sense point of view. The basic fitness pays off long term as it gives a broader base upon which to build. Many intermediate bodybuilders have great difficulty increasing the intensity of their workouts because they are simply not fit enough in cardiovascular terms. Increased aerobic fitness leads to greater metabolic capacity, better recovery and lower body fat levels, so its importance should not be underestimated.

Pulse Rate

Having large muscles and being very strong does not mean automatically you are fit. In terms of practising different sports, fitness can be a very specific concept. Being able to run a marathon does not necessarily mean you are fit to get in the ring and box three three-minute rounds or wrestle or row or paddle a canoe. Likewise, being able to squat or bench press 400lb is no guarantee that you will be capable of running five miles. When discussing fitness here we are limiting ourselves to talking about cardiovascular efficiency coupled with generalized muscular endurance. This can be described as physical work capacity and depends upon cardiovascular conditioning and strength endurance rather than the capacity to generate brief displays of maximum explosive strength or speed.

The benefits of being fit are numerous, but from the bodybuilder's point of view, the most important consideration is that it increases your capacity to train harder with shorter rests between sets to increase the intensity of workouts and accelerate the body's metabolism – all of which assists in burning stored body fat and improving definition.

Cardiovascular fitness can be determined by using pulse rate as a guide. In order to improve your fitness, you have to get your heart into its optimum aerobic training range and maintain it there for a minimum of twelve minutes. The optimum aerobic training range is between 60 per cent (low intensity) and 80 per cent (high intensity) of your maximum working pulse rate. An exact test of one's genuine maximum working pulse rate is very complicated and requires trained personnel to administer. As a general guide the easiest way to proceed is to subtract your age from 220 (your hypothetical maximum pulse rate) and consider the remaining figure to be your maximum working pulse rate. So a twenty-year-old will have a maximum working pulse rate of 200, a thirty-year-old 190, and so on. In the case of the twenty-year-old, this means working at a steady rate with a pulse rate in the range of 120 to 160.

Working at the higher end of your working pulse rate leads to quicker improvements in fitness and physical work capacity, but is more demanding physically, so it is as well to build up gradually. A twenty-year-old beginner would start out doing twelve minutes per session of an activity like static bike, treadmill, stairclimber, rowing machine, skipping or jogging at a pace which would keep his heart rate over 120. This would then gradually be built up.

The same principle of overload applies in fitness training as it does in weight training. To keep improving, it is necessary to make the training demands progressively more difficult. Training three times a week this might mean increasing the exercise time by two minutes per week after the first week. In ten weeks, this would result in an increase to thirty minutes per day. At the same time it is possible to vary the intensity of the exercise. Someone already quite fit from having done a lot of sport might find twelve minutes at 60 per cent would have virtually no effect on their cardiovascular fitness and might feel better about working at higher intensity, say 75 to 80 per cent.

To introduce a bit of variety, it is also fun to vary the pace and intensity of the training so that your heart rate works throughout the training range during the course of the aerobic exercise. This is achieved simply by going faster or increasing the resistance. If out jogging this could mean putting in short bursts where you stride or sprint or include a hill or two in your routes. One method used by a lot of runners, based on interval-training principles, is to jog from one lamp-post to the next, stride to the next, then sprint to the next, keep jogging for the next two or three to recover, and then repeat. This type of training can also be done on a bicycle either on the road or in the gym.

If you are fairly heavy, it is probably not such a good idea to run on the roads, because of the stress on joints due to high repetition impacts. A better alternative is to run on grass or go to a local running track. A pair of running shoes with adequate padding is a good investment to help avoid strains and sprains. Fast walking is an alternative preferred by many older trainers because it is less traumatic. Steve Reeves an ex-'Mr Universe' who became crippled with arthritis in his forties and fifties following a cycling accident, recovered his health and mobility by walking at a march with hand-held weights. This kind of training has the advantage of being free, and if you run or walk from home there is no packing of bags or travelling involved. The general guide to correct intensity is that you ought to be able to maintain a conversation without getting out of breath.

In terms of frequency and intensity, it is important to balance your fitness training with your bodybuilding goals. If you do too much aerobic exercise, especially the high-intensity kind, it is very difficult to gain muscle and you may even burn some off. On the other hand, your bodybuilding goals may change and you may decide that you would prefer the smaller but muscular and defined look of fitness competitors rather than the massive powerful appearance of the hard-core bodybuilder. This is purely a matter of personal choice and taste which is entirely up to the individual.

An aerobic training effect pulse rate chart is as follows:

		Training range		
Age	MPR	60%	70%	80%
15	205	123	143	164
20	200	120	140	160
25	195	117	136	156
30	190	114	133	152
35	185	111	130	148
40	180	108	126	144

GENERAL ADAPTATION SYNDROME

General adaptation syndrome or GAS was coined by the distinguished physician and biochemist Dr Hans Serle. This term describes the process of stress adaptation undertaken by living organisms when subjected to one or more of the many and varied forms of stress which they encounter in the course of their lives. Stress is any outside stimulus that causes a change in homeostasis (the body's normal state of functionality), climatic changes, disease, physical danger, emotional involvements are all things that can affect that state.

Stress comes in many forms, some of which are positive and others which are negative in their consequences. A certain amount of stress in our lives is vital for normal healthy functioning. Exercise, when carried out intelligently, is an example of positive stress as it causes us to improve physically to meet the demands its performance places on us. Disease, injury, divorce and loss of a loved one are all negative forms of stress since they cause our state of wellbeing to deteriorate. The general adaptation syndrome was observed by Serle to consist of three distinct phases: alarm, resistance and exhaustion.

When the body is exposed to shock, it responds with countershock which leads into the resistance phase. In any stress situation, the body's initial response is a decrease in its capacity to handle additional stressors. Immediately after a hard training session you are physically tired and are actually weaker than when you began. Weight training is a catabolic process where heavy exercise leads to a breaking down of muscle tissue in order to perform the workload.

Your body, however, begins to repair the damage done to it by training when you rest and eat correctly. This is the resistance phase. It begins to rebuild the damaged muscle tissue, making it bigger and stronger than before so that it will become better able to cope with that kind of stress. This repair, or rebuilding, phase is described as the 'anabolic process' in bodybuilding. However an excess of shocks to the system or multiple shocks leads to an overload that the body's recovery systems cannot handle. Training when you have a cold or influenza virus is almost certain to overload the body's capacity to recover and instead of resistance leading to recovery you will move into the exhaustion phase.

Exhaustion can result from a single powerful stressor or multiple less-powerful ones. It is important to understand that as well as being capable of specific responses to individual stressors, there is also a generalized reaction to the overall situation. Emotional difficulties, problems with relationships, stress at work, examinations, being in a rush to get things done and minor illnesses or infections may be relatively trivial factors in isolation, but when they occur simultaneously the cumulative effect can be very serious. At particularly stressful times it may be necessary to eliminate certain stress-contributing elements for the sake of general wellbeing. Obviously it should be common sense to take a rest from heavy training if you have any kind of temporary illness. The kind of non-specific response being discussed here is not just a psychological one, but a global response to numerous different stressors and is something that affects the body's glandular and hormonal systems as well as the central nervous system.

Overtraining

One of the most important implications of GAS for bodybuilders is that more is not always better. Overtraining is a real danger that ought to be avoided and tends to occur most often at intermediate levels. It is not always obvious when overtraining is the problem. Even if everything else in your life is going perfectly you have to be aware of the dangers of overtraining. If you find yourself losing weight when you are not trying to, lack appetite, are not sleeping well, develop stomach acidity or gastric disorders, you may well be overtraining. Other symptoms that are indicative of overtraining include catching colds and minor bugs that seem to persist and take longer to throw off than normal, or just feeling permanently fatigued or off-colour. This is normally dealt with by resting, taking a holiday or completely changing your physical activity for a couple of weeks.

If you feel well enough in other respects but simply stop making progress, you may well be overtraining. It normally happens to people who are training five or six times a week or more. In the first instance try cutting back on the frequency of your sessions; try training three or four times a week for a while and see if the longer recovery times help.

What makes people overtrain? The reasons are a combination of psychological and physiological factors. There is a kind of mild addiction to the effects of exercise. The endorphins produced by the body to counter its painful effects are a drug like opium and have a tendency to make people feel well after exercising, giving them a natural high that can be mildly euphoric. This is one of the reasons exercise is so useful in combating depression. Feeling good after training can lead people to do too much, particularly if they have otherwise empty lives. Other people have a psychological need to feel the effect of training and get a pump, some need to see themselves pumped up to feel reassured about how they look – the power of insecurity should never be underestimated. Other people just try too hard because that is the way they go about things; they tend to burn out, injure themselves or in some cases go on to become champions in spite of everything they do wrong!

Most exercise physiologists describe the training process in terms of the the three-phase model proposed by Serle. The basis of all training is to select the right kind of stressors to produce adaptation, to provide a stimulus and elicit an effect. The skill in designing a programme lies in selecting the right stimuli for the desired effect.

GOING BEYOND SHAPING UP

Intermediate Routines

One of the most difficult tasks facing the intermediate bodybuilder is that of self-honesty and taking a good long look at what work needs to be done to improve the weak points. Bodybuilders feed on success. When the results of doing certain exercises become obvious, they are encouraged to keep doing the exercises responsible. When your chest starts to look big and muscular from doing bench presses and dips, you become convinced by those exercises and persevere with them. When you look at your body there is always the danger of dwelling contentedly on those muscle groups that are developing well and not taking any notice of the groups that lag behind. There are bodybuilders with skinny legs who never squat, who when they look at their bodies take off their shirts, but keep their tracksuit bottoms on; bodybuilders with 16-inch arms and 38-inch chests because they never work their backs and so on.

If you are happy with the way your body looks that is fine. Some people argue that developing the chest and back can make the arms look smaller, when what they want is an impressive pair of arms. If you simply want to look good in a T-shirt that philosophy is understandable. However, if you want to compete and perhaps win a show, it is totally unrealistic. When you get up on stage you have to show symmetry, proportion and total, all-over muscular development. Likewise, if you are big and strong looking, but your abdominals are invisible and you have love handles, then you have to be honest with yourself and recognize that you have a fat problem. Some very hard trainers have little or no discipline when it comes to diet. Not making the effort at the dinner table or in the kitchen is as bad or worse than not bothering to train for such people.

If you are feeling stale and unsure about the best way to make further progress, take a long hard look at yourself in the mirror. Ask friends or training partners for constructive criticism. Decide what needs to be done and go for it. Having a clear plan of action is much better for you than just chugging along eating the same kind and amounts of food and going through the motions in the gym. For some people, particularly those who have been training for three to four years, a forthcoming contest can be just what they need to focus their concentration and bring out the best in themselves.

The following consideration of some of the training principles and methods used and encountered in many gyms uses a lot of terminology popularized by the Weider magazines such as 'peak contraction' and 'giant sets' which are now widely used by bodybuilders in gyms the world over.

Workouts, Sets and Repetitions

Most people programme their training according to one of the schedules set out in Chapter 2 and do the individual exercises in sets of repetitions. 'Three sets of ten' or 3×10 as it is usually written down has been a standard notation for trainees, basic targets for decades. A typical training diary is filled with entries like 'Bench press 3×10 70, 80, 90kg. 2mr'. This means that in the bench press, three sets of 10 repetitions were performed: first with 70kg then 80kg then 90kg with two minutes rest between sets. It could just as easily read 'Bench Press 70–10; 80–10, 90–8. 2mr' which reflects the failure to get a tenth rep on the final set. This kind of simple shorthand makes it easy to keep a record of what you do.

This has many positive aspects. It allows you to organize the workload and gives you definite targets to reach, maintain and surpass. There is a danger, however, in becoming a bit of a slave to the set system. Some days you could easily do more reps or use heavier weights but do not do so because it is not what you had planned. Why stop at eight or ten reps if you are capable of going on and doing twelve or fifteen? Do not be a slave to numbers. Make each set an exercise in intensity and squeeze out as many reps as possible rather than stopping when you reach a certain predetermined number. How often do you do an exercise where you plan to do four sets of ten repetitions and find the last repetition of the last set fairly easy? If the answer is fairly often you could do with increasing your weights or the number of repetitions or reducing the rest time between sets. If you do not do one of these things you are simply going through the motions – which is all right for people on maintenance programmes, but not enough if you want to grow and put on muscle.

Instinctive Training

Being instinctive about training sometimes means changing your plans and doing the exercises sets and reps that you feel like doing at a given time. This does not mean being sloppy or unmethodical in your approach, but does mean writing down your exercises and the order that you do them in, together with sets and reps, after you do them, rather than beforehand. Following your instincts can help stop training from becoming boring and also allow you to adapt your workouts to changing circumstances, injuries, unexpected highs and lows. You may feel that certain exercises are not working that well for you or that some body parts are lagging behind others and need more work. Some of the best workouts happen almost spontaneously when a training partner says, 'Lets do pull-downs today instead of bent-over rowing and superset them with Arnold press'. Having an open-minded training partner who is willing to experiment and make contributions like this can be a great help.

Continuous Tension

Continuous tension is an important principle in bodybuilding and is vital to stimulating muscular growth. Continuous tension means 100 per cent concentration on every repetition. Rather than doing what a weightlifter does, which is to move the weight as quickly as possible to lift it as efficiently as possible, you do the exercise slowly and consciously concentrate on tensing the muscles being exercised as you do each repetition, keeping them tensed throughout the entire range of motion. Most people do this in an exercise like crunches where they can place their hands on the abdominals and feel the muscles squeezing and contracting as they do the exercise. Often, however, where weights are involved they concentrate more on successfully lifting the weight than on making the exercise as difficult as possible to produce the maximum bodybuilding effect. Twenty kilos can feel like a hundred if you concentrate on squeezing the muscles to the maximum throughout the entire repetition. Applying the continuous tension principle means completing the range of movement in all exercises, but not locking out at the top and taking a tiny rest before doing the next repetition, as is often the case in bench press or squat.

Peak Contraction

Peak contraction is a technique used to increase exercise intensity. Very simply, it means squeezing as hard as you can when the muscle is fully contracted, so if you do a biceps curl the muscle fibres are most fully activated when the arm is fully bent. At this moment, when the muscle is fully contracted, you should make an extra effort to squeeze harder to encourage maximum muscle stimulation.

Pyramiding

Pyramid training is a system that has been used successfully for building size and strength by generations of bodybuilders. It epitomizes the idea of progressive resistance, and gives quite a vivid illustration of how it works. Weights are normally calculated by first assuming your maximum poundage for a given exercise. Suppose you can squat 150kg for one repetition. After warming up you would do a pyramid based on the following: 10×100, 8×110, 6×115, 4×120, 3×125, 2×140, 1×150, 2×140, 3×125, 4×120, 6×115, 8×110, 10×100.

To keep the time taken to do this kind of pyramid within reasonable boundaries, the tip is often eliminated. Sets six, seven and eight with near-maximum poundages would not normally be done, as single and low reps with near maximum loads are potentially dangerous and best left to power-lifters. Many trainers would leave out the fifth and ninth sets if they were not feeling right too. These sets are normally only done as confidence builders after following a strength-development programme when trying to establish a new personal best, perhaps once every three months. Some bodybuilders prefer to think of the personal best concept as the maximum weight they can manage for a minimum of five or six repetitions and calculate their training poundages according to that figure. Some trainers prefer to do a pyramid ending on the single maximum repetition and leave out the descending phase. This is difficult to justify, however, since the descending repetition are the ones where you get the best pump and also develop greater confidence in handling heavy weights; 110kg does not feel quite as heavy after lifting 125kg.

Super Sets

The super set is a system used by intermediate and advanced bodybuilders to increase exercise intensity. In a super set, two exercises are combined without taking a rest between them. Sometimes the same muscle group is supersetted; at others, different muscle groups are worked alternately. A same muscle group superset would be triceps push-downs immediately followed by triceps kickbacks. A popular superset involving different muscle groups is bench press with lat pull-downs, which pumps up the chest shoulders and back together. Supersets can be devised in all sorts of combinations – the main limiting factor is your imagination. Going beyond the super set exercises can be grouped in threes, sometimes called a 'tri-set' or super-super sets called 'giant sets' can be performed where rest time is reduced to a minimum and the exercises are performed almost continuously, one after another. These are extremely intense forms of training requiring high levels of conditioning normally only undertaken by people at national and international levels.

Drop-downs

A drop-down is a method of training that can be used to try and squeeze a little extra intensity out of the final set in a series by reducing the weight in order to enable more reps to be done. As an example suppose that you can mange eight reps with 100kg in your last set of squats. Instead of stopping at eight your training partners would take off 10kg from each side, the lighter weight should then allow you to complete a couple more repetitions. As you again approach failure, they take off another 20kg and you should be able to squeeze out a few more repetitions. It is a useful training method, but it is most effective when training in groups of three. It is easier to do using machines of the multigym type of design because there is only one pin to move. Imagine you are doing a final set of lat pull-downs. Your absolute maximum for ten reps is 90kg, but by doing a drop down to 70kg immediately after your set with 90kg, without resting, you get a couple more repetitions and really make the muscles burn.

Forced Reps

Forced reps are a very useful technique to help the bodybuilder achieve maximum intensity in workouts. Take bench press as an example. Imagine you can get seven repetitions with 100kg unassisted. With a training partner on hand to spot for you, you can try to do three more reps. Your partner only helps you as much as you need to be to complete the reps.

A good training partner will just help to keep the bar moving through the normal sticking points but should not take the weight unnecessarily or lift the weight for you.

Negative Reps

Negative reps are an advanced and potentially dangerous training technique if proper procedure is not followed. The muscles are capable of lowering in a controlled fashion a heavier weight than they can actually lift. This eccentric phase of the exercise is a great strength builder, but of course there must be a competent training partner on hand – perhaps even more than one person if very heavy weights are being handled. The spotters help you to actually lift the weight and keep you covered on the descent phase where you lower it, as slowly as possible, resisting the descending weight all the way. They should only intervene to assist on the descending or negative phase if you get into difficulties. Spotters have to be alert and ready to intervene at the slightest hint of a problem whilst being careful not to overreact.

Cheating

Cheating is one of the most contentious exercise techniques. Its advocates, which include top expert bodybuilders like Lee Haney and Bill Pearl, say it is the most effective way of increasing the intensity of an exercise. Its detractors say it is just an excuse for sloppy exercise form and sooner or later leads to injuries. Correctly done, cheating makes it possible to squeeze out an extra couple of reps at the end of a set when it is impossible to continue to move the weight using strict form. The lower back and legs are often involved in generating extra power in exercises like the barbell curl or overhead pressing movements. If you want to cheat, do it properly, but not in every work out and on every repetition!

PRIORITY

Priority means identifying what your goals are, what your weak points are and concentrating on the body parts that need most work. If you have big arms but your chest and back are lagging behind a bit, give chest and back priority when the time to train comes. This can be particularly important if you are very busy with other things and cannot get to the gym as often as you would like to. Train the weakest body parts first, when your energy levels are highest for the greatest possible intensity. If you can only get to the gym twice in a given week because of other commitments concentrate on working the body parts that need to catch up rather than increasing the gap by doing your best parts.

INTENSITY

Intensity is the goal of most experienced bodybuilders in their workouts. They want to work the muscle until they achieve a pump and then go for the burn. The pump is the swelling and enlargement of the muscle groups as they fill up with blood forced into them to meet the demands of the heavy-duty exercise. The burn is the feeling that comes from extreme lactic acid production and is what causes intense exercise to become a painful experience, although most experienced trainers make a clear distinction between beneficial pain and damaging pain. Roberto Rosenburger once said: 'You have to be careful sometimes, because it is easy to go from a burn pain to a hurt, hurt pain.' His training partners at least knew what he meant. Arnold Schwarzenegger doubled his fame virtually overnight by saying 'A pump is better than an orgasm', which although a very subjective statement, that perhaps resorts to hyperbole, certainly indicates that some people do find the experience extremely satisfying!

4 Exercises

LEG EXERCISES

Most people when they take up bodybuilding tend to be much more concerned about the appearance of their upper bodies, particularly their chest and arms, than they are about their legs. As a consequence, they tend to concentrate their best efforts on training these showy muscle groups and put a lot less into developing their legs. This is a big mistake. A strong, well-developed pair of legs is the foundation for building a powerful, muscular, impressive looking upper body. Often sticking points in developing the upper body can be overcome by concentrating more on the legs and bringing them up to par.

The key exercises for ensuring steady leg development are the squat, leg press, leg extension, leg curl and for the lower leg standing or seated calf-raises and donkey-raises.

The Squat

The squat is the core exercise in any bodybuilding routine where the aim is to increase muscular mass and volume. It is, likewise, the basis of many strength and power developing routines where gaining weight is a definite aim. The serious trainee should invest in a good pair of weightlifting boots which have a slightly built-up heel to assist balance and provide sturdy ankle support. Another vital piece of kit is a weightlifting belt. The belt provides support for the lower back in some exercises, but in the squat its main function is to support the trunk and midsection thereby avoiding pulled abdominals,

strains, hernias and ruptures which can happen to even the most experienced trainers when heavy weights are handled.

Even for advanced bodybuilders great care must be taken when heavy weights are being handled. Attempting to train with heavy poundages too soon can be counter-productive unless adequate foundation training has been done. Chronic muscular soreness lasting anything up to a week is an indication that overtraining has taken place.

A prerequisite of safe squatting is a squat rack or at the very least, a pair of squat stands. These devices allow you to load the bar with whatever weight you can handle for the exercise, walk in, position yourself under the bar, lift the weight across your shoulders, step out away from the uprights and begin squatting. Without them, the amount of weight used is limited to what you can lift above your head and lower behind your neck onto your shoulders, or what a couple of training partners can support for you while you get under the bar into the correct exercise position. Generally, it is a good idea to walk in facing the rack, lift the weight and take a couple of steps to your rear so that there is enough space between the bar and the rack to allow a full squatting movement without any danger of the bar hitting the rack, rather than starting with your back to the rack then trying to walk backwards on tired wobbly legs after completing a tough set. Once the set is completed, returning the bar to the rack is also a straightforward process, as you walk forwards and can see where you are placing the bar. It is, nevertheless, always a good idea to have spotters on hand in case of unexpected difficulties. Some trainers with years of experience have had nasty surprises when squatting, by being overambitious and attempting to do too much. All sorts of factors can affect strength levels, such as dietary changes, illness, drinking habits, tiredness, training in a different gym, using a different bar, and so on. So it is important to be realistic and be guided by how you feel at the moment you do the exercise, not by how you think you ought to feel!

The Squatting Movement

Position yourself under the bar. Make sure the bar is not pressing down on the axial vertebra of the neck. It should rest comfortably across the lower part of the trapezius muscles and rear deltoids. The hands should be a comfortable distance apart.

Stand with the feet shoulder-width apart, toes pointing forwards and keep the back as straight as possible. Bend the legs at the knees, lowering yourself into the squatting position until your thighs are parallel with the floor. Push forcefully with both legs and exhale as you lift the weight, and return to the standing position. This constitutes one repetition.

Observations

Many beginners make the mistake of taking a relatively narrow grip because their shoulders feel strong and they feel they can push more forcefully, but in fact all they do is hunch their shoulders. It is a bad habit because they tend to be more aware of how their upper body feels when they should be concentrating on keeping a straight back and pushing with the

The squatting movement (1), with (2), (3), (4), (5) and (6) on following pages.

legs. As a result, they often get stuck in the bottom position and are unable to stand up with the weight because they still feel strong when their legs are exhausted.

Going any lower than parallel can place excessive compression on the knee joint, particularly if the squatter has big thighs and calves. So it may be inadvisable. It is important to keep the chin up and breathe in through the nose and out through the mouth. Those who tend to drop the head forwards, lead them to lose correct posture, placing undue strain on the lumbar region of the back, particularly when the legs begin to tire. It can be good discipline to fix the eyes on a point high on the wall in front of you in order to train you to keep the head up and maintain the straight-back position.

Some powerlifters employ a sumo-style wide stance when squatting. The idea behind this is that the wider the feet are apart, the less distance the weight will have to travel.

The relationship between force used, weight lifted and distance covered, means that moving a shorter distance will require less force to be used and therefore, logically, more weight can be handled. This kind of lifting technique requires supple, flexible joints as the joints support more of the weight. For this reason, it is not recommended. It tends to be regarded as counterproductive in bodybuilding terms, where the main aim is to make the muscles do the work, rather than the joints, thereby stimulating growth.

Checklist for Safe Squatting

• Good form. Ensure that your squatting technique is correct: straight back, hands a comfortable distance apart, legs bent to 90 degrees, thighs parallel to the floor, head up, breathe correctly, descend slowly and under control, never bounce.

- Avoid completely locking out and resting between repetitions unless it is absolutely necessary. Locking out transfers the weight from the muscles to the long bones of the legs and hip joints, reducing the intensity of the exercise. Maintaining continuous tension on the muscles increases the intensity of the exercise and achieves the same intensity with less weight and less repetitions.
- Spotters. Always have at least one and preferably two competent spotters standing by. A good rule of thumb is that the total weight of the spotters should match the weight on the bar!
- Adequate footwear and clothing – preferably weightlifting boots with built up heel for stability and ankle support, and roomy shorts or tracksuit bottoms that allow a full range of movement.
- Weightlifting belt – Always wear a belt that provides sufficient lumbar and abdominal support.
- Use a squat rack or squat stands.
- Knees. If you have knee problems or weaknesses, use knee wraps.
- Injuries. Do not try to squat if carrying an injury of any kind, particularly if the knees, legs, lower back, neck, abdominals or shoulders are involved.
- Olympic bar. If it is at all possible, use an Olympic bar for squatting. The spring in the bar makes it less of a dead weight and helps in overcoming sticking points. The best ones are the Swedish brand, Eleiko which are made of sprung steel and will not bend or break under the heaviest loads a human can lift.

Front Squat

The front squat is particularly useful for stimulating the front thighs and is a very good training discipline to teach correct squatting form.

The bar is taken from the rack or stands, the hands holding overgrasp, and is positioned high on the chest so that it rests on the collar bones while being careful to avoid causing any restriction in breathing. The elbows have to be lifted high and the fingers allowed to open so that the bar can be held in position by the extended fingers, rather than gripped. This position requires supple forearms and fingers.

An alternative method preferred by many trainees, is to get into position and fold the arms, keeping the elbows up high away from the body so that the hands hold the bar in position.

Beginners, in particular, reap long-term benefits from learning the front squat before the rear squat. The simple fact is that in order to do the movement correctly, the trainee must keep a straight back. Any forward bending, however slight, will cause the bar to fall off its supported position across the collar bones. By keeping a straight back, the lumbar region still works but it is not subjected to the kind of potentially injurious strains that may result from sloppy squatting technique. The legs are effectively isolated in consequence, and the thighs work harder than in the rear squat where the big gluteal and hip muscles tend to get recruited when the thighs begin to tire. If the novice bodybuilder wants to squat, it is a good idea to begin with front squats and spend at least three months before moving on to the rear squat.

The technique the majority of people prefer is to grip the bar and hold it in place with crossed arms when doing the front squat. Standing feet shoulder-width apart, breathe in through the nose and lower yourself into the squat position, making sure to keep the head up and the back straight. When the knees are bent at 90 degrees and the thighs are parallel with the floor, stop the descent and come back up into the standing position by driving forcefully with the thighs, exhaling as you do so.

Front squat (1), (2) and (3).

Hack Squat

The hack squat is usually done in a special machine. The machine is usually angled at about 70 degrees and has padded shoulder rests. You get into position, release the safety brake and lower your body into a deep squat position. As the footplate is angled to the same degree as the back rest, it amounts to doing a squat with a totally straight back. This exercise works hips, gluteus maximus and front thighs very effectively without the worry of having to balance a bar. As with all the leg exercises, varying foot positions will vary the effect of the exercise on the muscles.

Leg Press

The leg press is the strongest training movement for the legs. It is a very strong exercise in the sense that very heavy weights can be handled relatively safely.

Each machine has its advantages and disadvantages. There is a considerable variety of types of leg pressing machine. Many have some kind of locking mechanism for safety. This allows you to begin the set starting with the legs extended and lower the weight under control so that the first repetition of each set is an eccentric movement. This in turn allows the trainee to get used to the weight. Some machines are adjustable so that trainees of different heights, leg length and flexibility can set the machine up to suit their particular needs. Others are fixed designs for the average person and may cause problems for the very tall or short trainee. All machines can also be used for performing toe press which is a useful exercise for training the calves.

Prone Vertical Leg Press

This machine is the most primitive design but tends to be popular because it allows a big range of movement, allowing you to work the legs, hips and buttocks. It requires that you lie down underneath the plate where the weights are stacked. Normally you have to get into position to do the exercise with the legs in the knees-bent position, although some more modern machines have locking mechanisms to allow you to set the distance for your starting position before you begin.

Normally the starting position is lying on your back with your knees almost touching your chest. You should inhale and look up at the plate where your feet are resting. You push hard, exhaling as you extend your legs. With heavy weights many experienced body-builders prefer to be helped on the first repetition of each set to avoid any risk of straining and allow the muscles to get used to the weight on the descent.

Seated Horizontal Leg Press

This is probably the safest design of leg press machine and is found in many local sports centres, which have facilities based around multigyms, polygyms and the like. The machine consists of a stack of weights. The training weight to be used is selected using the selector pin and you sit in the chair and place your feet against the plate. There are often handles at each side of the seat to allow you something to grip. This helps prevent you from slipping in the seat as you take the strain. The legs work quite well with relatively little strain on the lower back because of the seated position, but the range of movement is not as great as with other machines, especially if you are tall or have long legs.

The exercise is performed by pushing with the legs to lift the weights stack and then allowing the legs to bend under control to lower the weights back into the starting position. The negative phase of the exercise on this machine is especially important and should take twice as long as the pushing movement used to lift it. Because of the mechanical advantage this machine tends to offer, it is particularly important to do the exercise slowly.

Inclined Plane Leg Press

The inclined plane leg press tends to be the machine preferred by serious bodybuilders. It combines the best of both worlds in as much as it allows a lot of weight to be handled without putting excessive strain on the lower back.

You sit in the machine with the legs at about 30 to 45 degrees to the floor when they are extended. The trunk is at 90 degrees to the legs and the back is flat against the padded back of the seat which is also angled. Ideally, you should begin the exercise with the legs extended and inhaling as you do so, slowly lower the weight until the knees bend as far as feels comfortable, usually just before the thighs touch the chest in a person with a normal range of movement. As you push to lift the weight by straightening the legs, exhale forcefully.

Horizontal Leg Press

This machine usually consists of a metal plate mounted between two uprights with three short bars for adding weight, one on top and one at each side, for even loading. You have to get down under the plate and lie on your back with your hips directly under the plate.

Inclined plane leg press (1) and (2).

This type of machine duplicates the squat action much more than the normal leg press. You select a weight by putting the selector pin in the appropriate hole in the weights stack. You then lie on your back on a padded bench, your feet on a metal base plate and your shoulders fit under a pair of cushioned rests that are attached to the padded bench. When you push with your legs, your shoulders press against the padded rests making the bench, which is mounted on rollers slide, in the direction you are pushing. As your legs straighten, a cable-and-pulley system comes into play so that the stack of weights is lifted as you straighten your legs.

Back Lying Vertical Leg Press in Power Rack

If you train in a gym which does not have a custom leg press machine the leg press can also be performed in a standard power rack by placing the bar in the low position normally used for partial dead lifts. Get on the floor directly under the bar, and with the hips directly under the bar, bend the legs and place the soles of the feet on the bar. Ensure that the lower back is kept flat on the floor. Push and straighten the legs, lifting and supporting the weight on the soles of the feet. Complete the repetition by allowing the legs to bend and slowly lower the weight until it returns to the starting position.

Lunges

The lunge is a complete exercise for the legs that tends to be relatively neglected these days. It is a difficult exercise in that it requires balance and coordination as well as good flexibility to do correctly. Because all of the major muscle groups of the legs are involved in the action, it is quite a demanding exercise in terms of the heart and lungs too.

Barbell lunges (1) and (2).

It is not necessary to use very heavy weights with this exercise. The ankle, knee and hip joints are all involved in this movement. The prime movers are the gluteus maximus, the quadriceps, the soleus and the gastrocnemius.

Always warm up and stretch the legs and hips before doing this exercise.

Barbell Lunges

Take a barbell and place it across the shoulders as you would if you were going to squat. Starting with the feet shoulder-width apart, inhale and take a long step forward on your left foot and slowly lower your body by bending the knee and hip of the left (leading) leg. If the step is the right length, your left knee should be directly over the toes of the left foot when you reach the lowest position in the lunge. Complete the repetition by pushing yourself back upright with the lead leg, and stepping back into the starting position.

Complete the repetitions for one leg and then do the same number on the other.

A variation on this exercise is to step through with the trailing leg after making the initial lunge and stand up, so that you complete the repetition a stride away from where you began. You can then either continue to step forwards doing consecutive lunges if there is enough space, or after completing your first lunge, step backwards into the lunge and then return to your original starting position.

Note: If when you do the lunge, the knee of your leading leg is over the ankle, you have either made too long a step or have not lowered yourself enough. This is usually a result of lacking confidence in your balance or of not being flexible enough. If your knee is well

79

Dumb-bell Lunges

The movement is identical to that described for barbell lunges, the main difference being that the arms hang by the sides. Beginners tend to prefer to learn to do lunges without weights initially, then use light dumb-bells before progressing to barbell lunges. Lunges with heavy dumb-bells is a hard, demanding exercise, which helps develop grip strength as well as developing strength and flexibility in the legs and assisting with thigh separation.

Leg Extension

The leg extension is a popular exercise, good for separating the quadriceps. Start by selecting the desired training weight. Then, sit upright on the bench, placing the feet under the padded cushion, with the legs bent 90 degrees at the knees. Tense the

Dumb-bell lunges (1) and (2).

past the toes, you have made too short a step, which is potentially a more serious fault because it places unwanted stress on the knee. Practise stepping into the lunge and checking your front knee position relative to your front foot in the mirror without using weights at first, just to get used to the movement and to learn the correct technique.

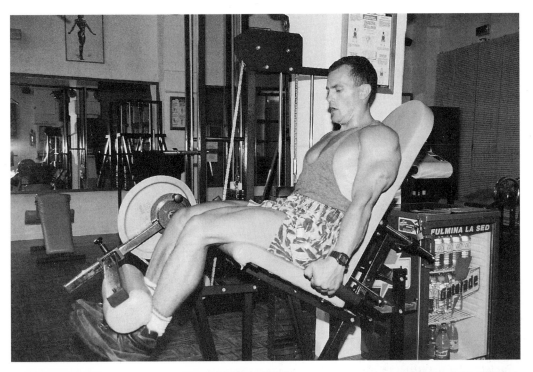

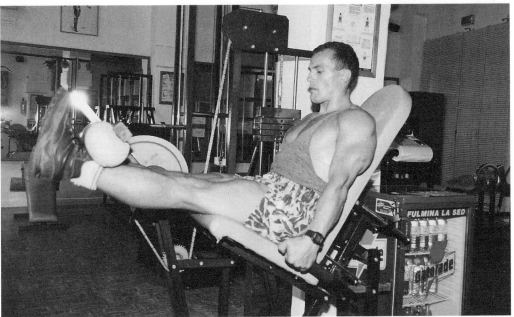

Leg extension (1) and (2).

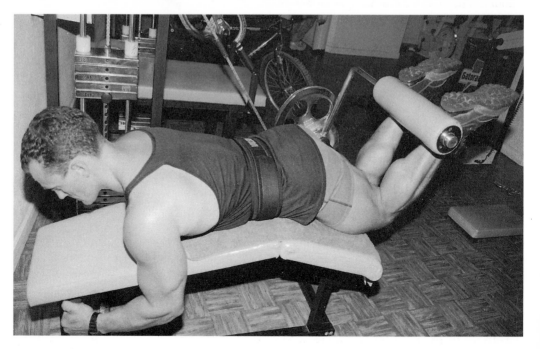

Leg curl (1) and (2).

quadriceps and straighten the legs, slowly raising the weight until the legs are straight. Hold the extension for a second or two and really tense the quadriceps to get a strong peak contraction. Keeping the tension on the leg muscles, slowly lower the weight into the bent leg position, without letting the weights touch the stack. Good form, meaning a well-controlled, relatively slow movement is much more important than lifting a lot of weight in this particular exercise. It is very good for stabilizing the knee joints after injuries.

In order to isolate the quadriceps still more, it is possible to do single leg extensions, working one leg at a time and really concentrating on the muscles being worked.

If you do not have access to a machine, the same exercise can be done sitting on an ordinary bench using iron shoes or boots, which can be loaded up with weight to the desired amount. These are a fairly antiquated way of training, and the boots normally have to be loaded up and strapped on, which is a bit laborious for those brought up on modern exercise machines. However, they can give very good results and are much easier to store in a cupboard, for example, if you are training at home.

Leg Curl

The leg curl machine is one of the most effective ways to develop the femoralis or thigh biceps. Some are simple flat benches with angled bars for stacking on discs, while others are more sophisticated, employing pulley systems with the bench raised and angled in such a way as to alleviate pressure that might be placed on the lower back as a result of poor posture or incorrect technique. There is a natural tendency, when the legs become exhausted, to try and shift the angle of the hips to gain more leverage, but this has to be resisted as it puts the thin sheets of muscle in the lower back (which can tear surprisingly easily) under a strain with which they are not designed to cope. Particularly when working on a flat bench, it can be a good idea to get a partner to hold down the hips to assist in isolating the thigh biceps.

The comments made about iron boots are equally applicable to this movement, although done prone, the exercise movement ceases to be effective once the lower leg passes 90 degrees. Thus, it is better to do the movement standing up, supporting your weight on one leg and holding onto something with your hands for balance. That way the thigh biceps have to work a lot harder, although it is often a good idea to have a training partner handy to help you through sticking points.

Stiff-legged Deadlift

The stiff-legged deadlift works the lower back and gluteus maximus rather than the thighs and hip muscles. It is, however, an excellent exercise for stretching the hamstrings and can be combined very effectively with leg curls for rear thigh workouts. 'Stiff-legged' is something of a misnomer as variations on the basic exercise exist which involve keeping the knees slightly bent.

To get a good stretch, this exercise is best performed standing on a wooden block about 6-inches thick. Stand with the feet a comfortable distance apart, but generally no wider than shoulder width.

If you stand keeping the feet together, the stretching effect on the hamstrings is greater, but keeping your balance is more awkward.

Stand upright, holding the bar just in front of the thighs with the arms straight using an undergrasp, overgrasp or mixed grip. Take a breath and bend forwards at the waist, allowing the hip joints to flex, and

Stiff-legged deadlift (1), (2) and (3).

slowly lower the bar, letting the arms hang straight down. Keep the bar close to the legs at all times. Large-diameter discs will touch the floor before a full stretching movement is reached, hence the block. Straighten up slowly using the muscles of the lower, back, gluteus maximus and hamstrings, inhaling as you come up.

This exercise can be performed with straight legs and a straight back, or bent knees and a straight back, or straight legs and a rounded back. It is also acceptable to use dumb-bells instead of a barbell.

The Good Morning Exercise

This exercise works the erector spinae of the lower back, the gluteals and the hamstrings. It should be done with a straight back and with straight legs. The knees can be slightly flexed to avoid any danger of hyperextending the knee joint, but the bent-knee position must be maintained throughout the whole range of movement so as not to begin lifting the weight with the front thighs and hips. It is a useful exercise for strengthening the lower back, but care must always be taken to warm

it is necessary to allow the hips to move back as you go down into the bent-over position. Slowly come back up to the starting position, inhaling fully as you straighten up.

CALF EXERCISES

For many people, calves are probably the hardest muscle group to develop in the whole body. To a great extent, it is a question of genetics and biomechanics. There are three orders of lever in the body and the calf connects the foot to the lower leg by a second-order lever, which is the most efficient in terms of generating strength. The calves have to support the weight of the body when walking and provide the power for the ankle joint to flex and extend when walking. This mechanical efficiency is a prerequisite for effective locomotion. The size of the calf muscles is determined to a large extent by, and where, the muscles attach to the bone. Some bodybuilders have high calves which, mechanically speaking, function very efficiently for high-repetition exercise. How many good marathon runners do you see with big calves? For the serious bodybuilder, having high calves is something of a curse, as it makes their development extremely difficult. Extremely difficult does not mean impossible though. The great Arnold Schwarzenegger had a lot of problems developing his calves to get them into proportion with the rest of his body, but through the winning combination of brutal intensity and perseverance, he was able to do it.

The opposite side of the coin is that those bodybuilders who are blessed with good calves tend not to have to do any more for them than any other muscle group.

The calf muscles consist of the gastrocnemius and the soleus. These muscles can both be worked by a combination of standing and seated calf-raises.

up properly and begin with very light weights. The exercise takes its name from the forward-bending movement typical of early morning callisthenics, toe touching, and the like.

The exercise is straightforward but care must be taken. Stand with the feet shoulder-width apart or slightly wider, and hold a moderately loaded bar across the back of the shoulders. Inhale, and, with a straight back and straight legs, slowly bend forwards at the waist, keeping the back flat and the head up until you feel a pleasant stretch in the back of the thighs and exhale. To keep your balance,

Standing calf-raises (1) and (2).

Calf-raises

Standing Calf-raises

Standing calf-raises are normally done in a machine which consists of a weights stack, an elevated footplate (sometimes angled) and a pair of shoulder pads. You select the desired weight position yourself, with the pads supported on the upper part of the trapezius muscles. Normally you have to bend your knees to get under the weight, and by straightening the legs you lift the stack some 6 to 9 inches, sufficient to allow for a full range of movement in the exercise. Press down with the toes and, keeping the legs straight, raise the heels and the balls of the feet clear of the plate. Go right up high on your toes and tense the calf muscles as hard as possible, holding the position for a second or two to get a peak contraction. Transfer your weight onto the balls of the feet and lower the heels as low as possible, stretching the calf muscles completely. It is important to keep the knees straight and the ankles, hips and shoulders in a straight line; allowing the hips to move forwards and backwards results in the lower back, hips and thighs coming into play and lifting the weight, which is counterproductive. Keep the body in a straight line and make the calf muscles do all the work.

Seated Calf-raises

Seated calf-raises are very good for isolating the soleus. Seated calf-raise machines normally consist of a weights stack or a bar on which to place discs, and a T-shaped padded bar which is placed across the thighs, just above the knees when you sit in it. The balls of the feet are usually perpendicularly below the knees on a raised block.

Always select the weight before sitting down and position the pads so that you are comfortable before starting to do the exercise. There is normally a release mechanism controlled by a handle of some kind which takes the weight until you are comfortably positioned. Once in position, release the handle, take the weight and press down with your feet, raising the heels off the ground and lifting the weights stack as high as possible. Hold the weight at the high point of the movement for a second or two to get a peak contraction and then lower it. Let the weight descend, under muscular control, until the heels go down as far as they can, so that the calves are fully stretched. Hold the stretch for a second or two, and then repeat the movement.

Donkey-raises

The donkey-raise is an exercise that is particularly useful if there is no calf machine available, since it performs the same function, but by making use of the body weight of one or more training partners. Execution is simple.

The person doing the exercise stands on a 4- to 6-inch high block, bends over at the waist and supports him/herself with the hands against a wall or on any appropriate piece of apparatus, such as the handles of a back-raise machine. The training partner climbs onto their lower back, sitting directly over the hips. For safety reasons, this should be done with some degree of care and never by jumping on leapfrog fashion. A hundred kilogram plus bodybuilder jumping onto the lumbar region could cause all sorts of damage, especially if their partner is not expecting it. Remember your training partner is not a horse and the spine can be easily damaged!

Once both partners are ready, you press down with the feet and push yourself up high onto your toes. Hold the top tensed position for a second or two, ensuring a peak contraction, then lower yourself until the calves are fully stretched. It can be a fun exercise to break up the monotony of training from time to time, and is a good one for developing camaraderie or injecting a touch of humour into a workout when motivation or energy is flagging.

SHOULDER EXERCISES

The shoulders are an important muscle group to develop in order to accentuate the width of the upper body. The combination of a narrow, trim waist and wide shoulders is one most bodybuilders and a lot of other people seek. The shoulders also play an important role in a whole host of sports as all throwing, punching and pressing movements involve transmission of power from the legs and trunk into the arms via the shoulders.

The shoulder girdle, comprising the clavicles (collar bones) and scapula (shoulder blades), links the arms to the torso via the shoulder cap and the shoulder, chest, back and neck muscles. The shoulder joint itself is

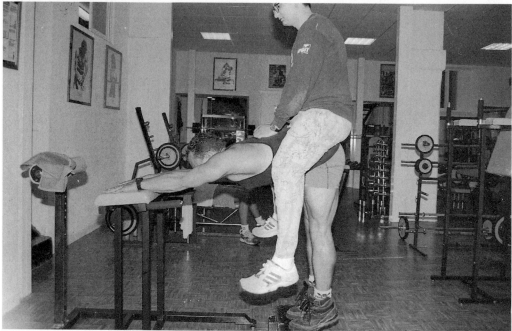

Donkey-raises (1) and (2).

controlled by a complex combination of muscle groups capable of a considerable range of complex movements. The joint itself is designed for mobility rather than stability and is prone to dislocation. The muscles of the shoulder comprise the deltoid, a large, thick, triangular-shaped muscle divided into the posterior, medial and anterior heads. These give the shoulders their rounded look. The rotator cuff muscles are four smaller muscle groups which actually move the joint and at the same time provide a certain stability. The rotator cuff muscles are the supraspinatus, infraspinatus, teres minor and subscapularis.

The pectorals, latissimus dorsi, trapezius and rhomboid muscles also come into play in making many other movements involving the shoulders, usually movements of the scapula or shoulder blade. It is important to bear in mind the interrelatedness of shoulder, chest and back muscles when selecting exercises and the order in which to do them.

Military Press

This is a basic shoulder building exercise which directly works the front deltoid, the muscle responsible for shoulder adduction. The triceps

Military press (1) and (2).

89

are also brought into play for straightening the elbows and the trapezius controls the upward rotational movement of the shoulder. It can be done standing or seated, the important point being to keep the back as straight as possible. Taking an undergrasp, support the bar across the upper chest on a line with the collar bones, and tilt the head only slightly backwards to allow room for the bar to pass without touching your chin or face. Inhale, and tense the abdominals and the muscles of the upper back to provide isometric support, and immediately push with the shoulders to lift the bar above your head. Do not push the bar forwards as you begin to press; concentrate on driving it directly upwards at a slow-to-medium speed. Lower

the bar slowly under control back to the collarbone resting position, lightly touching the chest before beginning the second repetition. This exercise can also be performed on a variety of machines, some of which ensure a very strict movement, although the difficulty of balance and coordination of the lifting action is removed.

Hyperextending the spine by leaning back brings the larger, stronger pectoral muscles into play, but transmits excessive shearing forces into the lumbar region of the spine. This was the reason this exercise was removed from the Olympic Games' weightlifting programme as it is inherently dangerous, especially when heavy weights are being handled.

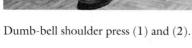

Dumb-bell shoulder press (1) and (2).

Dumb-bell Shoulder Press

This is basically the same action as the military press but by using dumb-bells, a slightly greater range of movement may be achieved. It is usually done seated with a bench angled at 90 degrees to prevent any kind of leaning back or cheating by bending the knees and using the legs. (Bending the knees while standing and using the legs for extra thrust is an old Olympic weightlifting assistance exercise known as a 'push press', which can help weightlifters develop their power for the clean and jerk, but the bodybuilder should be more concerned to isolate the shoulders and concentrate on making the deltoids do the work, rather than trying to lift heavier weights.) Keep the back flat up against the bench. The dumb-bells are held with the hands pronated, just as with the barbell exercise, but the arms should be at 90 degrees, parallel to the head, the dumbbells almost touching as you receive them from your training partners. Inhale, and slowly lower the dumb-bells down to the shoulders allowing the arms to come apart as the elbows go down and out away from the body. When the dumb-bells reach the shoulders, stop the descent and begin pushing them back overhead, exhaling as you do so. As the pushing action is completed the hands draw closer together until the dumb-bells touch in the fully extended position with the arms at 90 degrees.

Beginners often prefer to do an alternate pressing movement, using first one arm and then the other, as it is easier in terms of balance and coordination and allows them to get used to the exercise. Where heavy dumb-bells are being used, it is a good idea to have two spotters who can hand you the dumb-bells simultaneously with your arms in the extended position. This way your muscles get used to the weight as you lower it into the starting position for the first repetition.

Shoulder pressing movements can also be done on a variety of machines, which because of the mechanical leverage advantages that they provide, usually allow for more weight to be lifted.

Arnold Press

This movement is a modified dumb-bell press that was invented by the great Arnold Schwarzenegger. It is designed to isolate and increase the stretch on the front deltoid. The starting position is the same as for the standard dumb-bell press, but instead of lowering the elbows to the sides they are brought down in front of the head, supinating the hands as you do so, until the dumb-bells reach the starting position in front of the chest. To raise the dumb-bells exhale, and push the dumb-bells up in front of your face, the palms of the hands facing towards you and pronate in the final 6 inches of the movement.

Arnold Press (1), with (2) and (3) overleaf.

This is a great exercise for developing the anterior deltoids. It is more difficult than the normal dumb-bell press because you have less leverage, so lighter weights are recommended initially.

Press Behind Neck

The press behind the neck is done using a barbell held behind the head. The shoulders are pulled back so that there is greater use of the trapezius which rotates the shoulder girdle upwards as the arms extend overhead.

Take a wider than shoulder-width grip so that when you hold the bar either on your chest or behind your head, the wrists and elbows form a perpendicular line at a right angle to the floor. Too narrow a grip will be uncomfortable and will prevent a complete range of movement being performed. Lift the bar overhead and slowly lower it behind your neck, inhaling as you do so. When the bar touches the trapezius area, exhale and push it directly upwards until the elbows straighten overhead.

This exercise is not recommended for anyone who has had any kind of neck or shoulder injury or similar problem.

Lateral-raises

The lateral-raise is a basic shoulder exercise that can be done standing, seated or lying face down on a bench, either prone or

Press behind neck (1) and (2).

angled. The angulation of the body and the grip used are very important as they determine which areas of the deltoid get worked. Like flys, it is one of the exercises most people do not do very well. Most people use too much weight, do the exercise too fast, and swing the dumb-bells up in cheating fashion using the back muscles. Spending a little time to understand the correct technique and concentrating on good form pays dividends.

The basic movement is done seated or standing with a straight back. Hold a pair of dumb-bells at your sides, with the palms of the hands facing the thighs and the thumbs pointing forwards. Keeping the arms straight and elbows fully extended, inhale and lift the dumb-bells to the side (abduction) until your arms are horizontal to the floor. Hold this position for a second or two, then lower the dumb-bells slowly back to the starting position, exhaling as you do so. Do not allow the dumb-bells to touch the thighs as this relaxes the tension on the deltoids.

Lateral-raises (1) and (2).

Frontal-raises (1), (2) and (3).

To shift the emphasis of the exercise onto the side deltoid more, bend the upper body forwards slightly, about 5 degrees – no more. Pronate the hand so that the palms face to the rear and the little finger edge of the hand is pointing laterally outwards. Raise the dumb-bells as before, making sure to keep the thumb pointing down to the floor and the little finger edge of the hand pointing to the ceiling. It is advisable to try this with a lighter weight than used for normal lateral raises as it is a considerably weaker movement. Do the repetitions very slowly with a peak contraction at the top of the movement and you will feel the rear deltoids begin to burn.

Lateral raises are excellent exercises for working the whole deltoid as well as the rotator cuff muscles. For the latter reason it is often prescribed using light weights as a rehabilitation exercise. Another therapeutic variation involves describing two large semi-circles by taking the weights overhead and touching the backs of the hands together, then slowly lowering them in front of the body

Frontal-raises

As its name suggests, the frontal-raise involves lifting a barbell or dumb-bells in front of you.

95

It is an exercise that develops the anterior deltoid.

Hold the bar or dumb-bells with the hands pronated, palms facing the front of the thighs. Raise the weight using straight arms until it is just above horizontal to the floor, and hold it straight out in front of you for a second or two before slowly lowering it again. This movement can be done using cable machines too.

CHEST EXERCISES

A well-developed chest is one of the most striking features of a good body. A big chest gives an impression of size and power even when dressed.

The relationship between chest size and waist size is an important one because the narrower the waist, the bigger the chest will appear to be. The chest muscles include the pectoralis major, the pectoralis minor, subclavius and serratus anterior (serratus magnus). The pectorals are the show muscles of the chest and have an upper half connected to the clavicle and a lower half that is connected to the sternum or breast bone. The pectorals connect to the upper arm just below the front deltoid and are the muscles that pull the arm across in front of the body. The serratus muscles cover the rib cage.

Bench Press

The basic bench press is a very effective exercise for directly working and developing the pectoralis major chest muscles. As the shoulder girdle and elbows also move the front deltoid and triceps are also worked indirectly in this exercise, it is a very strong movement and considerable weight can be handled. It is the basis of most strength-development routines

Bench press (1), (2) and (3), with (4) overleaf.

for the upper body because the synergistic effect is the greatest and the maximum number of muscle groups are involved in making this large pushing movement. The basic grip is with the hands slightly wider than shoulder-width apart and the elbows directly under the bar. Too wide a grip places an inordinate strain on the wrists and can cause tearing of the rotator cuff or pectoral muscles. A very narrow grip makes it into a triceps exercise.

Lie down on the bench with your back completely flat and feet shoulder-width apart to give you a stable pressing base. Powerlifters often assume an arched back position in order to handle maximum possible poundages but this is neither necessary nor desirable for bodybuilding purposes. Take the bar from the supporting stands and press the arms out straight. A competent spotter can be of considerable assistance at this stage of the exercise and in guiding the bar back into the stands or

rack when you complete your set and when the arm and chest muscles are tired and not coordinating quite so well. Inhale, and as you do so lower the weight under control until it just touches lightly on the chest. You should only feel the bar, not the weight, which should be supported by the muscles. Keeping the lower back pressed flat onto the bench slowly press the weight off your chest, straightening the arms and pushing upwards. Keep the feet flat on the ground and the hips on the bench. Avoid bridging to bring the lower pectorals into play. The direction of the push should be slightly towards the upright rests at the head of the bench.

Lowering the weight slowly is a very important part of the exercise as it allows the muscles to get used to the weight in a gradual way and reduces the strain on ligaments, tendons and joints caused by ballistic movements. Try to imagine the weight is the heaviest thing you have ever lifted; this can assist in activating as many muscle fibres as possible. When the bar touches your chest, keep the tension in the muscles. Do not relax and let the weight rest on your chest as this can cause damage to soft tissue, intercostal muscles, cartilage and even the ribs if you are unlucky. The correct line for the movement to follow in basic bench press means that the bar should lie across the chest parallel with the nipples.

Some advanced trainers occasionally lower the bar to the collar bones, to isolate the pectorals more, but it must be said that having a loaded bar anywhere near the throat area is potentially very dangerous. It takes relatively little pressure to cut off the air supply to the lungs and brain by squeezing the neck, causing rapid unconsciousness. A loaded bar could crush the trachea like an eggshell and in such a case would kill you by choking you to death. Consequently, the bench press to neck version of this exercise should never under any circumstances be attempted without competent spotters being on hand and should never be taken anywhere near failure. It is a banned movement in some gymnasiums where serious accidents have happened. Overconfidence and being overenthusiastic has caused a number of deaths in this way, so be warned! In any event, it is completely unnecessary. If you feel desperate to stretch and isolate the pectorals, use dumb-bells as the element of danger from asphyxiation is completely removed.

Tip: When heavy weights are being handled spotters should always be present.

Dumb-bell Flys

This exercise works the pectoralis major and anterior deltoid. It is good for stretching the chest muscles and the shoulder/chest tie-in. The active joint is the shoulder. The elbows are kept slightly flexed throughout the exercise so there is a certain amount of isometric work being done by the biceps and triceps.

Lie on a bench with the feet shoulder-width apart and hold the dumb-bells at arm's length, directly above your chest, about 10-inches apart, keeping the elbows slightly flexed. Slowly lower the dumb-bells down and out, away from the body so that the chest opens fully. Inhale as you start to lower and control the weight, by using muscular contraction of the chest and shoulder at all times. When the fully stretched position is reached, you should feel the pectorals being stretched and be aware of where they connect to the sternum. Bring the dumb-bells back to the starting position, again slowly pulling them up and towards each other. Exhale as you raise the dumb-bells back to the starting position, so that you are ready to breathe in again at the beginning of the next repetition. Do not hold your breath. The downwards or eccentric phase of the movement is just as important as the upwards or concentric phase.

As with all exercises where the active joint is working in extension, it is important to do the exercise movement slowly and under control at all times. This is not a particularly strong or safe exercise, so fast movements and heavy weights are not recommended. It is best used as a stretching and pumping movement before or after heavier work such as a bench pressing movement.

Dumb-bell flys are particularly useful for working the chest and shoulders in cases where an elbow injury or soreness may prevent you from doing other exercises. They are also a useful exercise for pre-exhausting the pectorals before doing bench press.

Pec Deck

The pec deck is an excellent machine which duplicates the flying movement to a certain extent, but it allows you to perform the action

sitting upright and with fully bent rather than almost straight arms. At the moment when the pectorals are peak contracting the weight is not supported by the arms, so it is a more intense and specific exercise for the chest.

Sit in the machine with the back flat against the backrest and the feet flat on the floor. Place the hands and forearms in the right starting position depending upon the arrangement of pads and handles, and exert force with the pectorals to bring the pads together in front of you. This is the starting position. Inhale as you allow the weight to take the arms out and back in a semi-circular movement, resisting the pull of the weights slightly with the chest muscles. When both elbows align horizontally with the shoulders, begin to exhale and bring the arms back in front of you by contracting the pectoral muscles. Complete the repetition by touching the forearms together in front of you, and hold for a second or two for peak contraction as you finish exhaling. The pec deck does not involve any elbow-joint movement or strain at all, and is a good exercise for pumping and isolating the chest.

Inclined dumb-bell flys (1) and (2).

Pec deck (1) and (2).

Inclined press (1), (2) and (3).

Inclined Press

The inclined press is a modified form of bench press normally performed on an adjustable bench. Some benches allow the exercise to be done standing up, but the vast majority are designed so that you sit down and lean against the adjustable back. Benches can normally be angled at 30, 45, 60 or 90 degrees. At 30 degrees, the exercise closely resembles the bench press although more stress is thrown onto the upper chest. However, the steeper the angle, the harder the anterior deltoid works and the less the pectoralis major is involved in the movement. At 90 degrees, the movement is very different and is called an 'overhead' or 'shoulder press', being almost completely a shoulder exercise. The elbow joints, shoulders and shoulder girdle are all involved in performing this exercise.

To begin the exercise take the bar in the finishing position, with the arms straight directly overhead. Inhale, and as you do so, slowly lower the bar until it touches the upper chest, collar bones or shoulders. Keeping the forearms perpendicular to the floor, exhale and press the weight overhead. Resist the temptation to push the bar out away from your chest as this will lead to a loss of control and may cause you to drop the weight. The most important aspect of the exercise movement is that the bar should travel in a perpendicular, straight line relative to the floor.

Some benches have adjustable stands or racks; others do not. In either case, one or two spotters on hand can be a big help as they can assist with helping to lift the weight into position initially and returning it to the rack or floor. For a slightly increased range of movement, dumb-bells can also be used and many manufacturers produce machines which can duplicate the motion, although the exercise feels quite different without the problem of balancing the bar or dumb-bells where you also have gravity to contend with.

Decline Press

Decline press is a useful exercise to change the angle of the normal bench press and it engages the lower chest, front and rear deltoids. Usually it is a fractionally stronger exercise than the normal bench press and allows heavier weights to be handled. The downwards angle of the decline bench is normally only about 15 or 20 degrees below horizontal and spotters are essential for safety reasons. The movement should be perpendicular and at 90 degrees to the floor.

Dips

Dips either between parallel bars or on a bench are a really effective all-over upper-body exercise. The position of the hands and angulation of the body determine whether the exercise hits mainly chest, triceps or deltoids.

Dips between Parallel Bars

Grip the bars and support yourself on straight arms. Slowly let the arms bend and lower yourself between the bars, breathing in as you do so. When the arms form a right angle, push yourself back up, exhaling as you do so, until the arms are completely straight. The movement should be straight up and down. Avoid swinging forwards and backwards and try to keep the body as straight as possible.

Dips between Two Benches

Isolating the triceps obviously makes the exercise a lot harder and is usually done with the hands close together on a bench behind the body. The feet are supported on another bench, rather than between parallel bars. The feet on the bench supports part of the body's weight.

Pull-overs

There are two basic forms of pull-over: the straight-arm pull-over and the bent-arm pull-over. These are completely different kinds of exercise, despite the fact that both exercises work chest and back muscles simultaneously and that they have the word 'pull over' in the names. Superficially, these are apparently similar movements, but the feeling in both exercises is completely different.

Straight-arm Pull-over

The straight-arm pull-over is an excellent stretching movement for the chest and upper back. The serratus and abdominal muscles are required to work isometrically too, so it has a toning effect on them. It is the best exercise of all for expanding the thorax and ribcage, so it is a particularly important movement for young bodybuilders keen to develop a big chest.

Pull-overs can de done lying on or across a bench, using either a barbell or a dumb-bell. Most people seem to find the dumb-bell variant more comfortable as it puts less strain on the wrists and shoulders. If using a barbell, a pronated grip is preferable. If using a dumb-bell, form a triangle with the hands so that the finger tips grip the rim of the dumb-bell, and the thumbs press against the bar. Lying with the upper back flat on the bench, press the weight above the chest or have a partner hand

Dips between two benches (1) and (2).

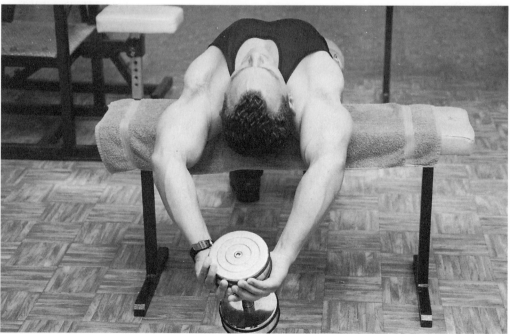

Straight-arm pull-over (1), (2), (3) and (4), with (5) overleaf.

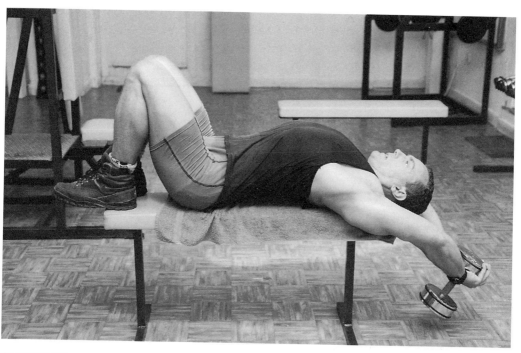

it to you in this position. Hold the weight at about 85 degrees and tense the pectorals, and then inhale as you slowly lower the weight in the direction of the floor, allowing the chest to open and the arms to lower. Keep the arms as straight as possible, as if you were lifting your arms above your head to reach up and touch something high up. As you lower the weight, the strain switches from the chest and deltoids to the latissimus dorsi muscles. Shoulder and upper-back flexibility determines how far you can lower the weight, but most people can go some way beyond 180 degrees. Aim to get a good stretch on the lats, then slowly lever the weight back up, tensing the pectorals when you return to the top position.

If done slowly and strictly this is a very demanding movement. It can have a very beneficial effect on the breathing mechanism and can be used with light weights to rehabilitate the elbows after injury since it helps strengthen connective tissue also.

Bent-arm Pull-over

The bent-arm pull-over is a power-building exercise for the prime movers: the pectorals, latissimus dorsi and posterior deltoids. Whereas the straight-arm pull-over is a leverage exercise which does not permit very heavy weights to be handled, the bent-arm pull-over can be used to develop considerable 'close to the body' pulling and pushing power in a way not duplicated by any other exercise.

Lie on your back on a bench and hold the bar at chest level with a narrow grip, with the hands between 3 and 9 inches apart, whatever distance you find most comfortable. Lift the weight a few inches away from the chest and push it towards your head. The bar passes within an inch or so of your face as you lower it past the top of your head and down towards the floor. The arms should be kept bent at the elbows at all times but allow the weight to slowly stretch the lats as far as possible before pulling the bar back up, over your face again and back to your chest. Inhale as you lower the bar and exhale as you pull it back up. If you find the grip on a straight bar uncomfortable experiment with a cambered E-Z curl bar.

Cable Cross-overs

There are number of varieties of this exercise. It can be done standing, seated on an inclined bench, or prone on a flat bench, depending upon exactly what effect you wish to achieve.

The big advantage that cable cross-overs have over all other chest exercises is that they allow a true peak contraction of the pectorals. It can be a very important exercise for developing the upper chest if done correctly. The key point about the movement is that it does not need to stop at 90 degrees as most of the others do, but can be continued, by allowing the arms to cross and really achieve a peak contraction of the pectorals.

Standing Cable Cross-overs

Step into the cable cross-over machine and take hold of the handles which are attached to lateral overhead pulleys. Stand with the arms extended laterally in the crucifix position, but make sure the hands are turned so that the palms are facing the floor and keep the arms slightly bent at the elbows. Inhale and lean forwards slightly, for balance and stability, then begin to exhale as you pull the handles down towards each other by contracting the pectorals. When the handles meet in front of your lower abdomen, squeeze the pectorals as tightly as you can and then allow the weights to draw your arms back up to the crucifix position, inhaling as you do so.

Cross-overs Prone or on an Angled Bench

If the cross-over frame has floor-level pulleys, you can do the exercise lying flat or leaning back at an angle. The procedure and breathing is the same as for the previous exercise, the major difference being that the hands are supinated because you are lifting up rather than pulling down. This is an extremely satisfying movement as it allows the arms to move well past the position achieved in an exercise like dumb-bell flys, allowing for a peak contraction of the upper pectorals that is otherwise virtually impossible to achieve. The cables mean the tension is kept right on the muscle at the moment of peak contraction, whereas in flys, for instance at the end of the movement, the weight is really taken by the arms. This is a highly recommended exercise for intermediate bodybuilders who want to improve their upper chests and pec/delt tie-in.

BACK EXERCISES

Arnold Schwarzenegger once said: 'The single most dramatic feature of a great physique is a well-developed back'. Many people neglect back development because it is not a showy muscle group. They tend to think that when you meet someone, dressed for an everyday social situation, nobody looks at your back. Chest, abdomen, arms if you are wearing a T-shirt perhaps – but not the back. The back, however, adds dramatic width to the physique and balances chest development. Anyone thinking of competing must work hard and use a variety of exercises to develop a wide thick back.

The main muscles in the back are the latissimus dorsi, the trapezius and the erector spinae. The trapezius is important for its role in lifting the shoulders and providing anchorage and stability for the neck, and is best trained by doing upright rowing and shrugs. The erector spinae, as the name suggests, are

Cross-overs prone or on an angled bench (1) and (2).

what allow us to stand up straight. They stretch from the sacrum to the skull, but tend to be hidden by the superficial muscles. They are easiest to feel in the lumbar region when doing hyperextensions or stiff-legged dead-lifts.

The biggest and most impressive muscles in the back, however, are the latissimus dorsi. There are two basic actions which develop the latissimus dorsi. One is the chin-up or pull-down action which strengthens the pec minor as well as the lats. The other is a rowing movement which works the latissimus dorsi and posterior deltoid as exemplified by seated or bent-over rowing. Because of the way all the muscles are interconnected, working the back usually involves a considerable amount of arm and shoulder work.

The Back-raise

This exercise is sometimes described as a hyperextension. When done correctly, this is

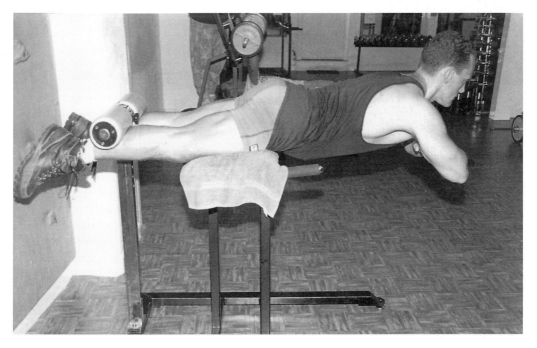

The back-raise (1) and (2).

one of the most beneficial back exercises known. Many athletes and ordinary persons, who have suffered from different kinds of lower back pain, have found it to be extremely helpful in relieving pain and muscular tension and for toning up the erector spinae and lumbar region in general.

Athletes in sports like gymnastics, wrestling and judo which require considerable suppleness in the back do hyperextend, arching the back and raising the trunk above 180 degrees. However, this is a highly specialized movement that should not be undertaken without adequate preparation and specialized coaching. It is unnecessary for normal bodybuilding or fitness purposes. People over thirty-five just starting to train to tone up and get fit should under no circumstances attempt to duplicate such a strenuous and potentially injurious movement.

Chins

The chin is one of the most effective ways of developing the upper back. All you need is a sturdy overhead bar and you can begin developing a great back and impressive biceps without touching a weight! Average-sized people who are reasonably strong can incorporate them into a training regime fairly quickly. If you only have time to do a single exercise for upper back and biceps the close grip chin is the best candidate. The biceps quickly get pumped as well as the upper back having to work.

As a basic guideline, the wider the grip, the less work gets done by the arms and the greater the intensity of the exercise for the latissimus dorsi. Wide-grip chins are very useful for widening the lats and the whole shoulder girdle is made to work. They are,

Chins: close grip chin, undergrasp.

Chins: standard grip chin (above); wide grip chin to back of neck (below).

Chins: close grip chin to back of neck (above); close grip chin with special handles (below).

however, more difficult than close-grip chins because the arm muscles are not so involved and they often prove too much for many beginners.

To do a basic wide-grip chin, reach up and take a pronated grip (overgrasp) on the bar. (If the bar is very high, you may need to jump or step up onto a block or bench.) You should be able to hang in a relaxed fashion without your feet touching the floor. From this hanging, fully stretched position, pull hard using your back and arm muscles to draw yourself up so that your arms bend and your chin (or better still, your chest), touches the bar. Squeeze the arm and back muscles for a second in this position. Inhale as you pull yourself up, and exhale as you lower yourself.

Any kind of pull-up or chinning movement, undergrip, overgrip, wide grip or narrow grip, may be very difficult if you are heavy. Fat, overweight people in particular are well advised to develop their back strength by doing lat pull-downs if they are unable to get more than five repetitions on the chinning bar. A surprising number of overweight people are unable to do a single chin because a few extra pounds makes a huge difference in this exercise. If you fall in this category do plenty of lat pull downs, front and back and try different grips. At the same time cut back on your calorie intake and lose a few pounds and in a matter of three to six months' training, most people find they can chin the bar for at least five repetitions.

If you are strong enough, the lats can be made to work harder by pulling yourself up until the back of your neck touches the bar, rather than your chest. Make sure that the lower body does not move and that the back generates the pulling power to do the exercise. To make the exercise even more difficult for the very strong, weight can be added by hanging a disc or a dumb-bell from a weightlifting belt, taking care to make sure it is securely fixed of course. A tiny minority of freakishly strong individuals, something like one person in 200,000, can do one armed chins, but a one-armed chin is a remarkable feat of strength and is not really a realistic goal for the majority of people training in gyms. Fortunately, it is not a prerequisite for developing a great body or for being a good bodybuilder.

Lat Pull-downs

The lat pull-down is done on a machine and works the same muscles as chinning a bar. It has the advantage of allowing the less strong to select a weight that they can handle in order to build up their strength to be able to do chins. There is normally a weights stack attached to an overhead bar via a cable and pulleys. The best designed machines allow you to sit on a variable-height seat and place your thighs under an adjustable padded locking mechanism. This means that as you begin to work with near body weight or more than body weight, you can anchor yourself to pull the weight downwards without being lifted up yourself.

Pull-down to Chest

Grip the bar, and sit down, making sure that the arms can extend fully so as to get a complete stretch of the upper back. Inhale as you pull the bar down towards you, and push your chest out as your elbows pull down and back. Keep your trunk straight and avoid leaning backwards. Try to bring the bar to your chest and squeeze with the upper back muscles for a second or two. Slowly exhale as you let your arms straighten, controlling the weight as your arms return to the stretched position.

Most lat pull-down machines offer a degree

115

Lat pull-down to back of neck (1) and (2).

of versatility many people do not explore. It is also possible to lean back at 45 degrees and do a modified pull-down which is more similar to a rowing movement, but which places no strain on the lower back. If you do this exercise, maintain the 45 degree angle throughout the set. Movement of the trunk is a form of cheating, using the body weight to build up momentum to get the weight moving, instead of generating the energy by pulling and squeezing the latissimus dorsi. If done with a wide grip, it duplicates the bent-over rowing action; with a narrow grip it is more like seated rowing. The grip can be supinated or pronated for variety.

Lat Pull-down to Back of Neck

Lat pull-downs can also be done to the back of the neck. It is important to keep the trunk as erect as possible when doing this exercise and many people like to reverse their breathing, inhaling as they pull down and exhaling as the arms straighten. If you are correctly positioned, it should only be necessary to tip the head slightly forwards. You should not be bending at the waist and hunched over. If you find yourself doing this, you are using too much weight or are incorrectly positioned in the machine, or both! The pull-down to the back of the neck is a weaker movement than the pull-down to the chest, so it is normally necessary to use less weight.

Rowing

Bent-over Rowing

Bent-over rowing is used to widen and thicken the upper back and to build greater density in the lower back. The prime movers in this exercise are the latissimus dorsi and the posterior deltoids. Some bodybuilders feel it is best done standing on a bench or block in order to allow the latissimus dorsi to fully stretch and to involve the lower trapezius and rhomboids which control the forwards – backwards movement of the shoulder blades. However, if your balance is not very good it can be done standing on the floor with good results. The knees should be kept slightly bent, the lower back flat and the chin up. Take a wider than shoulder-width grip and stand with the feet shoulder-width apart. Inhale and pull the bar up to your midsection, try to hold it there and squeeze the back for a second to get a peak contraction. Lower the bar slowly under control, exhaling as you do so. Normally, rowing is done with a pronate grip, but this can be reversed to add variety.

Bent-over rowing can also be done with dumb-bells, either lying face down on an inclined bench, which removes all the strain from the lower back, or by doing single-arm sets. For single-arm rowing, you should keep the feet square and support your weight by leaning on a bench with your free hand. Allow the shoulder to drop to pick the dumb-bell off the floor, but as you pull the weight up to the side of your midsection, keep the lower back flat, avoid twisting the shoulder girdle also.

Some people pull the weight to the side chest and twist the shoulder girdle as they do so. This is a power movement appropriate to certain sports, involving the posterior deltoid and erector spinae muscles more. This movement does not isolate the latissimus dorsi as effectively and is potentially more dangerous.

For many people, bent-over rowing is an uncomfortable, hard exercise because you are bent over in a position that makes breathing difficult and with heavy weights,

Bent-over rowing (1) and (2).

Dumb-bell rowing on a bench (1) and (2).

Seated pulley rows (1) and (2).

T-bar rowing (1) and (2).

it places a lot of strain on the forearms, hands and lower back. For all these reasons, it is very important to observe good form throughout the exercise.

Seated Pulley Rows

Seated rowing using cable-and-pulley devices is quite different in feeling from bent-over rowing, mainly because the hands tend to be closer together. The arms thus become more involved in the pull. Nevertheless, the prime movers in any rowing exercise are still the latissimus dorsi and anterior deltoid.

When doing seated pulley rows, keep the knees slightly bent so as to avoid undue strain on the lower back; try for a good stretch in the lats each time your arms straighten. Avoid cheating by using the lumbar region to generate momentum, the trunk should be kept almost straight throughout the exercise and there should only be minimal head movement.

T-bar Rowing

A more primitive form of rowing involves using a T-bar, where weights are loaded onto one end of a bar, the other end of which fits into a

123

Upright rowing (1) and (2).

purpose-built hinged frame. You stand astride the bar with the knees slightly bent, and pull the weighted end up to your lower abdomen or chest by performing a rowing action.

Upright Rowing

Upright rowing directly works the trapezius and deltoids as well as the elbow flexors. Some bodybuilders consider it to be a shoulder exercise, others like to include it in their back workouts.

Grip the bar in the centre with the hands about 4 inches apart and stand with the bar against the thighs. The grip must be pronate,

as this movement is impossible with an under-grasp. Slowly pull the bar in a straight line, letting the elbows go out to the sides, keeping them high and the wrists relaxed. Inhale as you pull the weight upwards. Pull the bar up until it is just below the chin and hold this position for a second or two, then slowly lower the weight back down.

For the exercise to be really effective, it is important that the elbows be high and the trunk should be kept straight. Do not allow the body to bend at the waist and avoid bending the knees to get the legs into the movement. Some people find it more comfortable to have the thumbs along the top of the bar and others prefer to do the exercise using dumb-bells.

Shrugs (1) and (2).

Shrugs

The shrug is primarily an exercise for the trapezius muscles. The bar is normally gripped overgrasp and held level with the tops of the thighs. Breathe in and lift the shoulders as high as they will go, keeping the arms straight. Then pull the shoulders back as far as they will go and slowly begin to breathe out as you allow the weight of the bar to pull the shoulders back down and around into the original starting position.

Shrugs, although normally performed with a straight barbell, can also be done with dumb-bells, adding variation to a movement a lot of people find uncomfortable.

NECK EXERCISES

The neck is a body part that frequently gets neglected in many training programmes, although a number of standard exercises such as crunches, sit-ups, shrugs and squats do involve tensing the neck muscles in such a way as to develop them. There are many much better direct-stimulation exercises though. The wrestler's bridge and the headstand are both useful, but should never be undertaken without competent supervision. Using a partner with a towel or a head harness and isometrics, pushing your hand against the side of your head and resisting with the neck muscles can all help develop a big, powerful neck.

ARM EXERCISES

Big arms are usually the first attribute that novice bodybuilders set their heart on. The arms are generally the only body part that are regularly uncovered in everyday life and in popular culture tend to be the symbol or sign of physical strength. The time-honoured request of 'show us your muscles', usually involves bending the arm and tensing the biceps. The thing to remember about training arms is that the biceps, while being the show-piece muscle when the arm is bent, is only a relatively small muscle and 70 per cent of having big arms depends on well-developed triceps muscles. The biceps has only two heads, as the name implies, and the triceps has three.

The deltoid muscles also play an important visual role in giving an impression of size. The key, however, is to aim for a proportioned development of the various muscle groups. If the deltoids are especially well-developed, but the biceps are just average, they will appear even smaller.

Triceps Exercises

Close-grip Bench Press

The close-grip bench press is a strong triceps exercise. It differs from the standard bench press, which mainly stimulates chest development in that you take a narrow grip, generally slightly less than shoulder-width apart, keeping the elbows close to the sides of the body as you lower the weight to the upper stomach area. The effect of this is that the elbows bend considerably more and the triceps do a lot more of the work involved in lifting the weight.

Close-grip bench press (1), (2) and (3).

Triceps extension (1) and (2).

Triceps Extension

The triceps extension, correctly executed, requires that the elbow be the only moving joint. The exercise can be done with bar-bells, dumb-bells or on a variety of machines. The important point is to isolate the triceps and make them do all the work for maximum stimulation. There tends to be less stress on the wrists when using a dumb-bell for this exercise.

Grip the dumb-bell in the same way as for straight-arm pull-overs, and press it from your chest to overhead. If you prefer to do this exercise sitting down with the back supported by a 90-degree incline bench, have a partner hand the dumb-bell to you with the arms in the extended position. Breathing in as you do so, slowly lower the weight behind your head by allowing the arms to bend. Only the elbow joint should move, although the trapezius and deltoids are engaged isometrically in keeping the shoulders raised. When the arms are fully bent, exhale and drive the weight back up by contracting your triceps to straighten the arms again. Do the movements slowly, concentrating on good form. Have a competent spotter on hand.

Triceps Kickbacks

The prime mover in this exercise is the triceps. The dumb-bell kickback is good exercise for stimulating long head triceps growth because it promotes a peak contraction, when the arm is straight, but without the weight being supported by the skeleton or the joints. Normal triceps exercises involve a weight being pushed overhead against gravity, but when the arm is fully extended, which is where the peak contraction should occur, the skeleton and joints come into play and take the strain off the muscles.

Triceps kickbacks (1) and (2).

Hold equal-weight dumb-bells in each hand, and bend forward at the waist. Raise the elbow so that it forms a straight, horizontal line with the shoulder parallel to the floor. The forearm should hang at 90 degrees to the elbow joint. Slowly straighten the arm, lifting the weight by contracting the triceps, so that the dumb-bell also forms a horizontal line with the elbow and shoulder. Only the elbow joint should move; the shoulder should be held still. Slowly lower the weight under control by bending the arm until it returns to 90 degrees. Then stop. It is very important not to go past 90 degrees because then there is a slight pendulum effect and the dumb-bell swings as you start the next repetition.

The momentum from the slightest swinging movement takes the stress off the triceps, so it is very important to aim for perfect technique in this movement. Experiment with different degrees of pronation of the hands to see how the different parts of the triceps are affected – palm up, little finger up and knuckles up for example. These small details can make a big difference to the effectiveness of the exercise for many people.

Triceps Push-downs

The triceps push-down is only possible using machines of the cable-and pulley type. The prime mover is the triceps. The grip can vary from having the hands only a few inches apart to shoulder width, and a variety of attachments are available including straight bars, angled bars, straps, ropes and handles which allow different variations. The basic exercise is done with a straight bar, although a lot of people find an angled bar more comfortable because it puts less pressure on the wrists.

Grip the bar and pull it down until it is parallel with the chest. The elbows should be pressed against the sides of the body. The trunk should be erect or inclined very slightly forwards; more importantly, it should not move in the course of the exercise. Breathe in. Then, as you push the bar downwards, by contracting the triceps, exhale. Squeeze the triceps when the arms are straight then inhale again as you bend the arms. Slowly allow the bar to come back up to the chest.

The triceps should provide all the power to move the weight. A common fault a lot of people have is that they move their body to get some help from the back or chest muscles. However, all that they are doing is decreasing the intensity of the exercise effect on the triceps.

Biceps Exercises

The biceps is a long two-headed muscle that connects the shoulder joint with the radius. It is the muscle that bends the elbow and supinates the forearm. The supination function, such as when you use a screwdriver or a corkscrew, is a very important one and should be taken into account when doing biceps exercises, particularly those involving the use of dumb-bells.

Barbell Curl

The barbell curl is the standard biceps exercise. The prime mover is the biceps, but the shoulders and back are also involved to a certain extent as fixators. In a strict curl, only the elbow joint should move and the biceps should contract to lift the weight. Stand with the feet shoulder-width apart. Take the bar with the hands holding undergrasp slightly wider than shoulder width and let the weight hang parallel with the upper thighs. Inhale, and contract the biceps so that the arms bend and lift the weight until it is level with the chest. The elbows should be kept against the

Triceps pushdowns (1) and (2).

sides of the body. Exhale, and slowly allow the arms to lower the weight, resisting the force of gravity all through the movement and maintaining continuous tension on the biceps.

Bending forwards at the waist and leaning backwards to get the back into the exercise are forms of cheating. To check that you are doing the exercise correctly, try it with your back up against a wall or get a partner to stand behind you and place their hand in the middle of your upper back. If you find you are forced to step forwards as you try to lift, it is because you are using your back.

Seated Dumb-bell Curls

Curls can be done standing with dumb-bells, but by doing them seated any temptation to cheat on the movement can be removed. The big advantage of adding dumb-bell curls to a workout is that they allow the arms to move further back and give the biceps a better stretch.

Sit with the dumb-bells hanging by your side, thumbs pointing forwards. Inhale, and bend the arms, lifting the dumb-bells forwards and upwards. At the half-way point, begin to supinate the hand so that the palm turns

131

Barbell curl (1) and (2).

upwards as the weight comes up to the chest. The further you twist the wrist as you supinate, the greater the peak you get on the biceps. Squeeze the biceps when the dumb-bells reach the top of the movement and then slowly lower them, breathing out as you do so.

The beauty of working with an angled bench is that it is possible to change the angle at which the biceps work. The standard exercise is normally taught at 45 degrees, but experiment with a variety of different angles from prone to 90 degrees. Avoid any awkward stresses on shoulder joints. In all cases try to fix the elbows so that only the forearms move and the biceps work at maximum intensity. If there is even slight movement of the elbows, it means the shoulders are doing part of the work and gen-

erating momentum, reducing the intensity of the effect on the biceps. Get a partner to squat behind you occasionally and to hold the elbows still, so that there is no movement to the rear, and you will realize how much harder the biceps have to work. As always, do not sacrifice good form for the sake of handling more weight.

Hammer Curls

The hammer curl is so named because it resembles the arm action used when lifting a hammer to knock in a nail. It is different from other curling actions because there is no supination of the biceps. The brachialis and flexors and extensors of the forearms are directly stimulated by this

Seated dumb-bell curls (1) and (2).

Hammer curls (1) and (2).

Concentration curls (1) and (2).

exercise which can be done standing or seated with an E–Z barbell or dumb-bells. Dumb-bells are better for the seated exercise as it is easier to fully extend the arms.

Sit with the arms extended, palms facing inwards, and slowly curl the dumb-bells upwards. Inhale as you lift the weights and be sure to keep the elbows in the same place throughout the movement. The contraction of the biceps is what lifts the weight, but there is no supination involved since the wrists do not twist as in the seated dumb-bell curl. Squeeze the biceps when the arms are completely bent, then slowly lower the weight exhaling as you do so.

Concentration Curls

The concentration curl is a popular exercise for improving the peak of the biceps and is normally done last in most biceps workouts. It is usually done in a bent-over or seated position and strict form is essential for it to be effective. The arm is allowed to hang in a fully stretched position. Then the dumb bell is slowly curled up to the shoulder by pure contraction of the biceps. The shoulder and upper arm should not move at all. Only the forearm moves, the elbow is the active joint and the prime movers are the biceps and brachialis.

Preacher Curls

The preacher curl is so-called because it is done on a special inclined bench which resembles a lectern where a bible is placed in church. It is a good exercise for lengthening the lower biceps. To fully isolate the biceps, it is important to get your body right over the bench so

Preacher curls (1) and (2).

137

Reverse curls (1) and (2).

that the elbows become the true fulcrum for the exercise. The body should not move at all. The pulling power should be generated by the contraction of the biceps. It is very important to raise and lower the weight slowly and have a spotter near to reduce the danger of tearing muscle fibres.

Start the exercise with the weight in the top position and inhale as you lower it, until the arms are fully extended and you can feel the stretch in the biceps. Exhale as you contract the biceps and lift the weight back into the starting position. A common variation on preacher curls using a barbell is single-arm concentration curls done on the preacher bench.

A good tip is to lean right over the bench to ensure that the shoulders are in front of

the bench and do not contribute to the movement. The upper arms are not meant to be the fulcrum in this exercise. A common fault is to hang back from the bench, pulling down and using the back of the upper arms as a fulcrum, and thereby use the weight of the body to obtain extra leverage. All this does is to shift the emphasis from the biceps and lessen the intensity of the exercise.

Forearm Exercises

Reverse Curls

The reverse curl is simply a curl done with the hand held in the pronated position. It can

Mantis curls (1) and (2).

be done standing or seated, with a barbell or dumb-bells. Although the biceps and brachialis muscles work to bend the arm, this exercise is not so effective for training biceps as the standard curling movements. However, its real purpose is to work the muscles of the outer edge of the forearms which are placed under stress because of the difference in the grip. Breathing is the same as for the standard barbell curl.

Mantis Curls

This exercise is a little known variation on the reverse curl. The only difference is that the wrists are kept soft and relaxed. This shifts the emphasis of the exercise to the inner side of the forearms and gives the forearms a fuller pump. It is a very useful exercise for developing grip strength.

Wrist Curl

This is an exercise for developing grip strength and for bringing up lagging forearms to par with other body parts, if necessary. It can be carried out using a barbell or dumb-bells.

With a barbell, sit legs astride, lengthways, on a bench and lean forwards so that the back of your forearms rest on the bench. Your hands should be in the supinated position.

Wrist curl (1) and (2).

Your wrists should be positioned on the edge of the end of the bench. Slowly allow the hands to drop and let the fingers slowly uncurl, so that you end up gripping the bar with just the lat joint of the fingers and the fingertips. Feel the stretch in the forearms and then slowly curl the fingers up, gripping the bar normally again, and lift the hands as high as possible without moving the forearm from its position flat on the bench. Tense the forearms as hard as you can as you do this last part of the movement.

Reverse Wrist Curl

This is similar to the wrist curl except that you start the exercises with the hands pronated, which in this case means the palms of the hands are facing the floor. The effect is similar to that obtained doing reverse curls.

MIDSECTION EXERCISES: ABDOMINALS AND OBLIQUES

Good abdominal development, a lean muscular torso, is probably the most attractive single aspect of a trained physique. Pot bellies are not usually considered attractive. A flat stomach, is particularly sought after by people as they get into their late thirties and early forties, since the natural tendency is for the belly to curve outwards from eating too much and not exercising sufficiently. The competitive bodybuilder has to develop all the muscle groups and the abdominals are no exception; a well-defined abdomen draws the eye and is essential to complete the overall impression of muscularity and strength.

Abdominal training methods are currently the most hotly disputed of all. There is a huge range of possible exercises for the mid-section and, in the quest for 'washboard abs', all sorts of combinations of exercises, sets and repetitions have been recommended. Many of these exercises have been criticized for being potentially injurious to the lower back. In particular, the sit-up, inclined sit-up, sit-ups with weights behind the head, and leg-raises. There is a physiological basis for this concern. The problem stems from the fact that the sit-up involves using the hip flexors as well as the abdominals to do the movement. The real problem is the way in which the psoas muscle (the strongest member of the ilio-psoas group) connects to the lateral sides of the lumbar region of the spine. The ilio-psoas and the rectus femoris are the prime movers, responsible for flexing the hip joint. The lumbar region of the spine has a natural tendency to curve inwards and the continued contraction of the psoas (which takes place when performing sit-ups) can increase this curvature to the point where it causes lower back pain. As a result, a number of specialist 'safe' abdominal exercise machines have been designed along with gimmicks of all sorts which have been marketed with the promise of rapid, safe and effective abdominal development.

The most important thing to remember is that, in the first instance, you should do all exercises in correct form. Obviously any exercise movement which causes you injury, excessive discomfort or simply does not feel right should be examined carefully and if not suitable, discarded. Some sources suggest that the damage caused is not immediate, but something that takes place over a period of years that may not manifest itself until old age. However, this is largely supposition, as no well-documented long-term studies of large control groups have been carried out. Bear in mind that the fitness industry is largely driven by the North American market and that fear of litigation in the USA is a major consideration. Exercise and fitness consultants therefore tend to be cautious when expressing their views on exercise safety.

There are undoubtedly people for whom doing sit-ups or leg-raises is synonymous with lower back pain. Such individuals may have to limit themselves to doing abdominal crunches, but should still be able to tone the abdominals quite effectively. We have never met anyone who has actually injured their back doing abdominal exercises although we have encountered some normal, healthy people who through performing the exercises incorrectly (usually doing sit ups with straight legs) have suffered from aches and pains in the lower back. This can be corrected by learning the correct technique and doing appropriate exercises for the erector spinae muscles. Doing sit-ups with bent legs rather than keeping them straight is quite an important precaution as it lengthens the lever arm for psoas pull, and the force required to make the hip movement is consequently reduced.

Of course, anyone who has any kind of medically diagnosed back condition falls in a completely different category. Slipped discs, spinal abnormalities and arthritic conditions of any kind have to be treated very carefully and only a qualified person should prescribe exercises for them.

A theory currently in vogue is that one of the major causes of lower back pain is the imbalance between the muscles of the lower back and the stomach, and to remedy this it is suggested that both muscle groups be exercised in the same workout. Some authorities suggest they be trained in super sets.

It is also important to realize that in order for your abdominals to show through, diet and body-fat levels are much more important factors than the training routines you employ. Everyone has abdominal muscles. What determines how impressive they look,

more than any other factor, is the amount of fat you are carrying. There are many athletes and sportsmen, particularly among the heavyweights with extremely strong, well-conditioned midsections, whose abdominals are virtually invisible. They look almost completely smooth because they have relatively high body-fat levels. Equally, there are virtually untrained individuals who, for reasons of diet and metabolism, are naturally lean, so their abdominals are always visible because there is very little fat covering them.

The following exercises can all be performed prone on an exercise mat or flat abdominal bench. The degree of difficulty or intensity can be increased in a number of ways: by doing more repetitions and taking shorter rests between sets, by doing them with weight resistance or by doing the exercise on an inclined plane, or a combination of all of these. Most abdominal boards or benches can be raised, usually by hooking them onto wall bars or a purpose-built ladder. The steeper the incline, the more difficult the exercise becomes. Well-conditioned athletes sometimes even perform sit ups hanging vertically from inversion boots, but this highly advanced exercise is inadvisable for most people.

Crunches

This is currently the most taught exercise for abdominals, simply because it is the least risky in all respects. Many people, however, perform the movement incorrectly. The key to getting the best out of this exercise is to maintain continuous tension on the abdominals and to really squeeze in the peak contracted position with concentrated intensity. Because of the continuous tension exerted on the abdominals, breathing tends, of necessity, to be shallow and rapid.

143

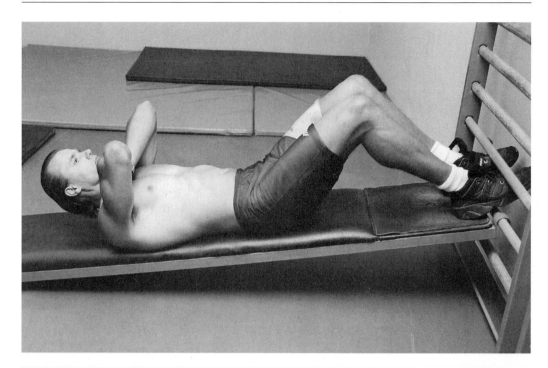

Crunches (1) and (2).

Sit-ups and Trunk Curl

The bent-legged sit-up is a popular exercise and as long as it does not cause any lower back pain, is a useful way of training the abdominals and many athletes use it as a general conditioning exercise, since it also works the spinal and hip flexors. It can be made harder by using an

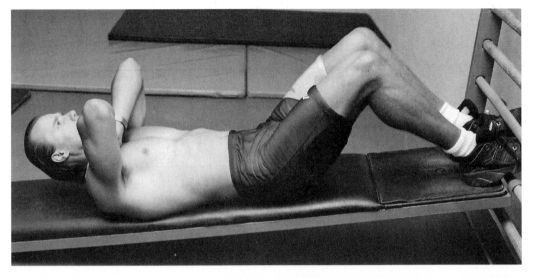

Sit-ups and trunk curl (1) and (2), with (3) overleaf.

inclined board, a Roman chair or by holding weights either on the chest or behind the head. Proper technique should be learned before increasing the intensity of the exercise. Sit-ups should not be done with the hands clasped behind the head as there is a tendency to pull with the hands and put a lot of stress on the cervical vertebrae, which can cause neck pain.

The most important aspect of correct technique in this exercise is to keep the lower back flat, initially, and curl the trunk, contracting the abdominals before allowing the lower spine to come off the floor. The feet should be secured and continuous tension should be kept on the abdominal. Exhale as you sit up and inhale as you lower yourself back into the starting position. The exercise can include a twisting movement at the end of the sit-up. Either touch the elbows to their opposite knees in a double twist before returning to the starting position or sit up and do a single twist, left elbow to right knee. Then return to the starting position before coming up and touching the right elbow to the left knee.

A further variation, preferred by some, is to come up to 60 degrees and hold the position so that the abdominals are under continuous isometric tension, and slowly twist at the waist from left to right, breathing rhythmically. The various twisting movements work the internal and external obliques.

If any of these exercises causes lower back pain you should stop doing it and try instead trunk curls where the lumbar region remains flat on the floor. The trunk curl is most effective if you lie flat with your thighs at 90 degrees to your back and the knees bent, the lower legs resting on a bench.

Leg-raises

Leg-raises involve considerable hip flexion but like the trunk curl, at least the lower back remains flat on the floor throughout the movement. Some people find it more comfortable to put their hands flat under their buttocks. Breathe in as you lower the legs, out as you raise them.

A less-strenuous version of the exercise, called the 'knee-raise', may be more suitable for many people. Lie flat on the floor with the legs extended and raise the heels just off the ground. Bend the legs at the knees and pull the knees towards the chest, keeping the lower back as flat as possible throughout the movement. As you lower the knees, straighten the legs. The feet should not be allowed to touch the floor so that the abdominals are kept under continuous tension.

Leg-raises and knee-raises can also be done on a flat bench, an inclined bench, supporting yourself on your elbows in specialist machines which have pads for the back and forearms, or hanging from an overhead bar.

Twists

Twists are an effective exercise for training the oblique muscles and can be done standing up, sitting on a bench or bending forward. Because this movement is done with virtually no weight, high repetitions are essential.

Doing twists with a loaded bar are potentially very dangerous for the lower back and spine and it is a useless exercise because most of the weight is driven by momentum generated in the initial stage of the movement.

Leg raises (1), with (2) and (3) overleaf.

5 Diet and Nutrition

INTRODUCTION

For the bodybuilder, the importance of correct diet and adequate nutrition cannot be overemphasized. Some bodybuilding gurus have even gone as far as to say that successful bodybuilding is as much as 70 per cent a result of diet, assigning to the training regimes and exercises a role of secondary importance. Bodybuilding, simply described, is about energy and growth. It is an equation. The bodybuilder needs fuel to provide the energy to power him or her through hard training sessions and a need for adequate rest to ensure complete recovery and growth. This recovery and growth can only occur if the body is properly nourished. The bodybuilder's metabolism and somatotype will influence the planning and composition of the diet, as will levels of physical activity outside the gym.

FOOD

In an age where everyone tries to look big and ripped all the time, diet planning is increasingly complex. For the professional bodybuilder who makes a living by entering and winning prize money in competitions, the benefits are obvious. Definition is all about metabolism and diet.

For the average person whose main aim is to improve physical appearance, it is not so obviously necessary. Everyone would like to be in the kind of condition displayed by top professionals like Dorian Yates, Flex Wheeler,

Paul Dillett and the like, but it has to be understood that these people have the most muscular physiques in the whole world. They are not the norm, they are superbodies, the product of many years of hard training and dieting, coupled to a scientific, often medically controlled approach and superb genetics. For many of us, food is one of life's great pleasures and it is often worth asking the question whether it is really necessary to keep body-fat levels to a minimum all the year round. It is extremely difficult to put on muscle and keep body-fat levels low at the same time.

Traditionally, bodybuilders used to bulk-up in the winter months, concentrating on getting bigger and stronger, eating plenty of whatever they needed to make sure they felt strong and powerful. As a rough guide, they would reduce calorie intake if the stomach muscles began to disappear under a veil of fat, but definition was not the priority then that it is now. Many of the top bodybuilders of twenty or thirty years ago look almost fat by modern standards, even when they were in contest condition. Even twenty years ago, top physique stars were sometimes photographed in relaxed poses in 'off-season' condition. This is no longer the case. Almost every photograph in magazines like Joe Weider's *Muscle and Fitness, Flex, Shape* or Robert Kennedy's *Musclemag* shows outstanding bodybuilders, both pumped and ripped. This leads the public at large to believe that bodybuilders are supposed to look this way all the time, something which is simply not possible. The number of intermediate bodybuilders who walk around tensing their muscles and flexing as if they were being judged in a competition at every moment is perhaps symptomatic of this view.

While it is true that many professionals and competitive amateurs no longer go in for bulking-up an then dieting to get cut for competition, preferring instead to stay pretty lean all the year around, it has to be understood that this requires considerable discipline and serious attention to diet, often scientifically or medically monitored. The amateur, depending upon how serious they are about bodybuilding – whether intending to compete or not, and other such considerations – has the choice of staying permanently lean or allowing a gain of a few pounds in the winter, over Christmas on holidays and so on.

If the main aim is to grow and put on muscle mass, trying to stay defined all the year round can prove extremely difficult. If you are inclined towards endomorphy, you are not naturally lean nor are you blessed with a fast metabolism, you can tend to get fat very easily if you eat the kind of food most people regard as normal – pies, cakes, ice cream, beer and other such forbidden delicacies. Obviously, if you intend to compete, you will have to make sacrifices, and deny yourself all sorts of foods. This is an inescapable fact. Ectomorphs too have their difficulties because it is often the case that they have to eat more than they would naturally be inclined to, and usually have to eat foods they do not particularly enjoy.

If you want to get big and muscular but not get too fat, a certain dietary moderation is the wisest course. The key really is in balancing realistic expectations with achievable goals, in both training and diet. Many of those who give up bodybuilding in the long term do so not because they stop enjoying the training, but because they find the dieting is often both punishing and expensive. There is a danger in being a perfectionist and in trying to emulate the routines and diets of top bodybuilders. Being obsessive about staying ripped can be very wearing on spouses, families and partners if they do not share the same enthusiasm for bodybuilding! Ultimately, being a little less ambitious can allow you to enjoy bodybuilding using natural methods into your old age, but you must continue to find it enjoyable and rewarding if you expect to stay motivated.

Good-quality healthy food does not have to be boring. With a little preparation and not too much effort, some very interesting and tasty dishes can be served up to meet the needs of the growing body as well as to satisfy the pangs of hunger and the taste buds.

COMPONENTS OF DIET

There are seven basic components to a healthy diet. These are proteins, carbohydrates, fats, water, fibre, vitamins and minerals. These seven components have different roles to play in nourishing the body and assisting muscular development.

Protein

Protein is essential for tissue repair and growth in the body and it is absolutely essential for building muscle. Protein is composed of carbon, hydrogen, oxygen and nitrogen and provides vital structural materials for metabolic enzymes that play a crucial role in breaking down fuels for energy when you train. Proteins are polypeptides made up of smaller units called peptides, which are amino acids. The etymology of the word derives from the ancient Greek word *protos* which means 'first', so its importance has been recognized for a long time. Protein-rich foods are the only ones that contain nitrogen. As nitrogen is excreted from the body every day, it has to be replaced.

The average person needs about 1g of protein per kilogram of body weight, the keen amateur bodybuilder needs 1g per pound and really serious bodybuilders require about 1½g per pound of body weight. There is a snag with this simple formula, viz. that it is calculated based on lean muscle mass. Fatter people have to consider how much of their weight is lean weight. Taking in more protein than the body actually needs will simply result in it being stored as fat.

The best sources of high-quality usable protein are white fish, eggs, poultry and meat. Fish is probably the best possible source of protein for bodybuilders because the ratio of protein to calories is extremely favourable. Eggs contain slightly more usable protein, but contain more calories too.

An essential part of protein assimilation is the production of hydrochloric acid (HCl). For the purposes of efficient digestion, however, increasing protein intake does not necessarily result in the body secreting increased quantities of HCl. Consequently it is highly recommended that anyone increasing protein intake takes additional hydrochloric acid digestive enzymes before each meal, to ensure that the extra protein is effectively assimilated. With sufficient HCl in the stomach, the effective assimilation of protein is as follows: eggs 88 per cent, fish 78 per cent, Dairy products 76 per cent, Meat 68 per cent, Soya Beans 48 per cent, whole grain rice 40 per cent, whole grain bread 21 per cent and white bread 20 per cent.

Carbohydrates

While proteins build muscles, carbohydrates power them. Carbohydrates are the energy source that fuel the body. Carbohydrates are obtained from foods rich in sugars and starches. Their digestion begins in the mouth and carries on through the small intestine and as the body begins to metabolize them, they are broken down into glucose which enters into the bloodstream where it is often described as blood sugar. Glucose provides the necessary energy for the operation of the central nervous system.

Any glucose which is not immediately used up by the body's normal metabolic functions is stored as glycogen in the liver and muscles. The body is only capable of storing very limited amounts of glycogen, the maximum amount being about 350g. About one-third of this glycogen is stored in the liver and is immediately available; two-thirds are stored in the muscles. Excess glycogen gets converted into fat and is stored as adipose tissue, which clouds definition and vascularity, so it is important to ensure your intake corresponds to your body's demands.

It is vitally important that you obtain your carbohydrates from unrefined sources. Refined carbohydrates are too much for the body to handle and usually come in foods with a high sugar content, accompanied by generous doses of fat, like chocolate, ice cream, cakes and biscuits. These refined carbohydrates are so concentrated that they overload the body's storage and utilization systems and initially cause a rapid increase in blood sugar. However, the body responds almost instantly to normalize the situation by producing insulin, which lowers blood-sugar levels. The idea that eating a bar of chocolate or a cake or taking glucose tablets before training gives you energy is totally wrong, and in fact, instead of giving you energy, just the opposite occurs.

Fresh fruit and fresh vegetables are among the best sources of simple carbohydrates and eating a pear, an apple or an orange half-an-hour to an hour before working out will provide you with usable energy for your workout.

Foods to avoid, because they include high proportions of refined carbohydrates, include cakes, sugar, sweets, pastries, pizzas, Chinese food, many pre-packaged fruit juices, and all kinds of tinned and prepackaged meals which tend also to have a high salt content.

Carbohydrates also affect your moods because they play a pivotal role in supplying the blood sugar that enables the brain and central nervous system to function. Eliminating carbohydrates from the diet completely is a totally negative dieting technique which will inevitably backfire; any weight lost will generally include a high percentage of muscle because the body needs the energy provided by carbohydrates for normal functioning. If it does not get it from food it will break down muscle protein to synthesize its own supply of carbohydrates. Carbohydrate deprivation also leads to fluctuating weight gain and weight loss. Determining what the right amount and sources of carbohydrates are for your body is a key factor in getting your diet right. It is as important from the point of few of controlling fat levels as protein is for building muscle.

Fats

Fats are an essential part of any healthy diet and play a vital part in many important bodily functions. It is used to help regulate body temperature and to insulate vital organs like the kidneys, heart, liver and even the eyeballs from physical shocks. It helps with normal tissue formation and supplies the energy needed by the cells for normal regeneration and reproduction. Fats, or lipids, as they are also called, once inside the body also serve as part of the transport and assimilation method for the liposoluble (i.e. fat soluble) vitamins A, D, E and K. Stored body fat is stored energy and even a lean body with relatively low fat levels contains twice as much energy stored as body fat compared with that stored as glycogen.

Fat is digested in a different way from either proteins or carbohydrates. It takes longer to digest and usually leaves you with a feeling of being full up for a longer period. It should never be eaten on its own as it is not fully digested without the presence of proteins and carbohydrates and can result in a build up of toxins which cause loss of appetite, headaches and queasiness. To be fully digested, it has to dissolve in the bile and interact with enzymes produced by the pancreas and the large intestine.

Although essential for certain bodily functions, a gram of fat contains about nine calories, which is more than double the amount contained in a gram of carbohydrate or protein. This high calorie content means that fat is an excellent source of energy, but on the other hand can be the bodybuilder's worst enemy in the battle for definition, since cuts and striations are a vital component of a winning physique in modern competition. Consequently it is important to keep the consumption of fats down to a minimum.

It is vital to be aware that most people consume a lot more fat than they might think, as it is present in many standard foods: olive oil, eggs, milk, cheese, butter, margarine, nuts, oily fish like mackerel and salmon, meat, poultry and even vegetables like avocados, olives and spinach. Vegetable oils are a healthier source of fat than animal sources, as vegetable oils like olive oil and sunflower oil are unsaturated fats, whereas sources of animal fat, such as dripping, lamb, beef, bacon and sausages contain saturated fats, which are high in cholesterol. Bodybuilders with slow metabolisms, who tend towards endomorphy, have to be particularly careful to monitor their fat intake as any excess can easily cause them to balloon up. Once formed, fat cells are extremely difficult to get rid of. Their number does not alter, they simply increase or decrease in size. The most effective way to burn fat is to combine aerobic and anaerobic training effects: training at a very fast pace, with minimum rests between sets in circuit fashion or using super and tri-sets, and even giant circuits with appropriate dietary adjustments.

Water

The body is approximately two-thirds to three-quarters water. There is water in every cell and between the cells. The average 70kg man contains about 45 litres of water. Water is the basis of the chemical solution which allows the multiple vital chemical reactions that life depends on to take place. Water is needed to maintain a correct balance of electrolytes within the body and for the utilization of minerals like potassium, sodium, calcium and magnesium which conduct electrical currents throughout the central nervous system, the brain and muscles. Most muscles are largely composed of water and it is essential that the body receives an adequate daily supply to ensure that it functions properly. Food consumed contains a certain amount of water but even so it is advisable to drink a further three pints a day, preferably spacing it out in the shape of eight to ten small glasses during the course of the day. If you are training hard and sweat a lot you may need to drink considerably more – as much as three litres. Avoid the temptation to replace lost fluid with fizzy drinks and beer because additives in fizzy drinks cause water retention and a bloated look, while alcohol uses up water in order for it to be processed by the body and may contribute to dehydration.

Some people like to work out well wrapped up and sweat profusely as they feel this helps eliminate toxins from the body. There is nothing wrong with this theory, despite the fact that training in plastic and rubber suits is often criticized as being pointless since any weight lost is only liquid and can be dangerous as it can lead to dehydration. These criticisms are correct if the person training is misguided enough to think that the point of sweating profusely is to lose weight and that it is important not to drink while training for that very reason. However, they miss the point that it can be a very good way of raising the metabolic rate, sweating out toxins, keeping warm and avoiding injuries and putting a little extra pressure into the workout to assist in focusing the concentration. Of course, small amounts of water should be drunk at regular intervals throughout this kind of workout to avoid any possibility of becoming dehydrated.

Fibre

Fibre is extremely important to ensure problem-free digestion and elimination of waste products, as it provides a certain amount of roughage for the intestinal muscles to work with in order to pass food through the system. If digestive or excretory problems are experienced try adding fibre to your diet: more high-fibre-type cereals for breakfast and more whole grain, wholemeal brown bread.

Vitamins

Vitamins are organic substances that the body's enzyme systems need in order to function correctly and a healthy person eating a well-balanced diet with plenty of fresh fruit and vegetables should be able to get their recommended daily dose from the food they eat. However, the stresses placed on the body by heavy training mean that for recovery and muscle growth to take place, higher quantities of vitamins than normal need to be consumed.

The basic vitamins are vitamins A, B, C, D, E and K. These belong to two classes: water soluble and fat soluble. The fat-soluble vitamins A, D, E and K can be stored by the body, but the water-soluble ones, B and C, cannot.

153

Vitamins B and C are key vitamins for the bodybuilder. Vitamin B6 has an important role to play in protein metabolism and amino acid assimilation. It is a natural diuretic with no negative side effects and helps transform glycogen into glucose for energy.

Vitamin C, although better known in connection with preventing colds and other minor infections, also plays an important role in stimulating synovial fluid production in the joints, and is instrumental in the formation and production of collagen, which forms the connective tissue of the skin, bones and ligaments.

The bodybuilder should aim to get plenty of vitamin C from fresh fruit and salads, as vitamin C gets lost when you sweat profusely. Rather than taking one large dose, take two smaller ones, one before training and one after. (If you do not want to take tablets, try eating an orange or two an hour before training and a grapefruit after.) You should also make sure that B vitamin intake is high enough by eating plenty of fish and eggs. Vitamin B6 and choline, another B vitamin are possibly the most important vitamins from the bodybuilder's point of view. Good sources of B6 are wheatgerm, sunflower seeds, brewer's yeast, and whole-grain rice with its husk. In hard training a supplementary dose of 500mg daily is recommended. Choline helps break down the accumulation of fats in the liver and breaks down arterial cholesterol. Brewer's yeast, liver and eggs are good sources of choline and which is unaffected by the cooking process.

As far as vitamin supplementation is concerned, more is not necessarily better. There are some people who suffer allergic reactions to megadoses of certain vitamins, so any increase in vitamin intake ought to be gradual and monitored. Try to eat fresh food as much as possible. The more raw, unprocessed food you eat the better, as this will make sure you get a healthy supply of the essential vitamins. An additional vitamin B complex tablet taken with choline and inositol can be taken if you feel your diet may be deficient in these substances.

Remember too, that drinking too much coffee (high caffeine content), alcohol, smoking and excessive sugar consumption are all factors that interfere with vitamin absorption.

Minerals

Minerals are necessary for the body to function healthily and they play an important role in bone and connective tissue regeneration and maintenance. The basic minerals the body needs are calcium, iron, potassium, magnesium, phosphorus, iodine, sodium, sulphur, chlorine, copper, manganese, zinc and cobalt.

For the bodybuilder, the most important of these are iron and calcium, as they are the ones most likely to be deficient in the diet. Women bodybuilders in particular tend to need more iron. Calcium helps avoid cramps and assists strength increases. An average bodybuilder usually benefits from 1,000mg of extra calcium a day, whereas an international competitor may need triple that amount.

Supplements

The supplement business is a huge money-spinner and a bewildering range of products is on offer to help bodybuilders, and anyone else, who might be interested in their pursuit of a better body. Unfortunately, the quality and effectiveness of these products is not standardized. Some manufacturers produce high-quality supplements, others less so. The vast majority of these supplements are far from essential for the average bodybuilder, although they can make up for dietary deficiencies in some cases. If you can afford them, by all means try them and see what effect they have on your body. They may just be an expensive indulgence or a waste of money in many cases. Be sure to write down details of diet and supplementation in tandem with training records and note how you feel form day to day in order to establish patterns. Remember that supplements are just that; they are not a replacement for a healthy diet.

Amino Acids

Amino acids are a popular and important form of supplementation, but many people are surprisingly ignorant of what they are and what effect they have on the body. Proteins are often described as the building blocks of the body, but amino acids can be considered as the building blocks that make up protein. There are twenty-two known amino acids which commonly occur in protein, eight of which are often termed 'essential'. The essential amino acids are so called because the body is incapable of manufacturing them itself, but can synthesize them from certain foods that are ingested. The eight essential amino acids are threonine, lysine, leucine, isoleucine, methionine, valine, tryptophan and phenylalanine.

The remaining fourteen amino acids, often termed 'non-essential' can be synthesized by the body from these eight. However, current research suggests that the distinction between essential and non-essential is fallacious. For the best possible physical well being, all of the amino acids ought to be obtainable from food consumed because the body, although capable of synthesizing the non-essential amino acids, may not be able to do so in sufficient quantities and may also put enzyme systems under undesirable strains as well as use up precious supplies of co-enzyme nutrients needed elsewhere. The other amino acids include hydroglycerine and hydroproline which are present in collagen and tyrosine and cysteine which are synthesized from from phenylalanine and methionine; the ten others which are present in most proteins are histidine, proline, serine, glutamic acid, glutamine, glycine, aspartic acid, asparagine, alanine and arginine.

These twenty-two amino acids can link and combine to create more than 50,000 different forms of protein. The body constantly breaks down the protein we eat into amino acid complexes, then recombines them to form whatever new proteins may be required for growth and maintenance. Amino acids undertake a host of functions too numerous to mention here, but in a nutshell they provide the raw material for repairing damaged muscle tissue and play a crucial part in enzyme production, building connective tissue, cell division, hormone creation for the regulation of bodily processes and even maintaining the genetic code.

A number of manufacturers make and sell specific free-form amino acids which means that they have been chemically separated from the long-chain proteins where they are normally found. They are best taken 45 minutes before a meal in pure white crystalline powder form, stirred into a glass of mineral water. Information about the specific qualities and effects of the individual amino acids are normally provided with the product.

SPECIAL DIETARY CONSIDERATIONS

Ectomorphs

Ectomorphs tend to be tall, nervous individuals with long bodies and long muscles. They have fast metabolisms and can eat virtually whatever they want without putting on weight, as they tend to burn up the calories they consume. As they tend to have little problem with maintaining low body-fat levels, they can benefit from taking additional calories in the form of liquid protein and carbohydrate drinks. In the old days, before the popularization of supplements, a popular method of gaining weight was to drink a mixture of raw eggs and milk after training to increase protein uptake. This fell out of popularity with the negative publicity that eggs received in the 1980s because of the dangers of *Salmonella* contamination which could cause food poisoning. Later discoveries about food allergies have led to milk and dairy products being taken off the list of recommended foods for many people as there is widespread allergy to them in adults.

Two or three months prior to a major competition dairy products should be completely eliminated from the bodybuilder's diet. Scientists have discovered that milk is extremely effective in promoting growth in children because they have an abundance of an enzyme called renin which, together with pepsin, allows them to fully break down and absorb the protein content of the milk. Many adults do not produce this enzyme in sufficient quantities to be able to fully assimilate the protein or properly digest the rest of the nutrients in the milk. This leads to it being stored as subcutaneous body fat. If you belong in this category, rather than piling on muscle by drinking numerous pints of milk, you will just succeed in hiding your muscles under a layer of fat. Many good bodybuilders have sabotaged their own best efforts to get defined because they lacked this information.

In order to gain weight, ectomorphs need to eat much more than their appetite indicates that they should. If you stop training for a couple of weeks and find that you tend to lose weight, you are almost certainly inclined towards ectomorphy.

Endomorphs

If you are the sort of person who rapidly puts on weight in the form of fat when you stop training, you are almost certainly inclined towards endomorphy. Weight gained when you do not train is usually a combination of fat and water retention.

As well as needing to do more aerobics to keep their metabolism high, endomorphs need to be very disciplined about what and how they eat.

Surprisingly, how you eat can be almost as big a factor in gaining fat as what you eat. Many endomorphs tend to rush their food in an anxious, hurried way, gobbling it down as fast as they can. This way of eating seems perfectly natural to them because in most cases, they have been doing it all their lives. In fact, it is learned behaviour and as such it can be modified. If you ever want to get defined you have to learn to eat in a different way.

Instead of filling your mouth with as much food as possible and gobbling it down, you should make a conscious effort to slow down the whole process. Take smaller bites and mouthfuls of food. After each mouthful, put down your fork or spoon and make an effort to chew the food in your mouth at least twelve times. Spread the food around inside your mouth and use the whole tongue to taste it. Swallow the food only after chewing it thoroughly and only then pick up your knife or spoon to take another mouthful. Many people simply stop talking at the dinner table when the food appears and get down to the serious business of sating their appetite, but this is counterproductive. Try to avoid eating alone and punctuate your eating with conversation to make the meal last longer. By slowing yourself down in this way, you actually spend longer eating and will feel fuller sooner. When you bolt your food, you quite often do not realize that you have eaten enough and continue eating more than you need. Your brain has not received the signal that you are no longer hungry and you end up taking in more calories than you need. An added benefit of modifying your eating habits in this way is that it will be a lot more pleasant for those people who are eating with you, so they too will probably enjoy their meal more!

The comments made about milk for ecto-morphs are doubly pertinent for the endo-morph, and if planning to compete, milk should be eliminated from the diet three months beforehand. Endomorphs should always take pains to avoid fatty foods. In the off-season, when training for size and mass, they should limit themselves to semi-skimmed or preferably skimmed milk on their cereals.

Endomorphic individuals not only have big problems with fatty foods, but also with refined carbohydrates. The craving for something sweet is an indication of low carbohydrate tolerance and in some cases can be so extreme as to be termed addiction. If you are the sort of person who has to have biscuits with a cup of tea or you buy chocolate or cakes and eat them when you are not actually hungry, usually between meals, you probably have an addiction to refined carbohydrates. This kind of problem can be overcome, but if it is not dealt with, it is extremely difficult (if not impossible) to get defined and may lead to serious health problems such as diabetes. The best approach is to eliminate as much sugar and salt from your diet as possible. When you feel a craving, eat an apple or a pear. Avoid having the kind of foods in your home that sabotage your efforts to get defined.

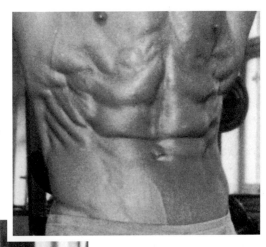

Main muscle groups of Dennis Oakes. (Above) abdominals; (left) side chest.

6 Competition

INTRODUCTION

Anyone picking up any of the current crop of bodybuilding magazines might be forgiven for thinking that competition is the be-all and end-all of bodybuilding. The truth is, however, that only a very small percentage of those people who get involved in bodybuilding ever actually take part in organized competition. All bodybuilders, however, are competitive. Some compete against their training partners, others against people that they don't really know but who they see every day in the gym and some enter shows to compete against other serious bodybuilders, hoping to be judged objectively, compared and found to be superior or better than the opposition. The most important competition all bodybuilders have however, is the one against themselves.

Life in many important respects is far from fair. Some people are more intelligent, some have more money, others are better looking, some are more gifted and still others are just happier people. One of the keys to being happy is recognizing what your gifts are and making the best use of them. In bodybuilding circles, the most important gift is good genetics. People who have never seen the top bodybuilders up close do not realize what 'good genetics' means. There are a gifted few, natural mesomorphs who will thrive and grow on virtually any kind of training regime or diet. At the other end of the scale are the hard gainers, individuals who go through all sorts of punishing regimes and dietary torments over long periods of time to make only

very slight progress. The majority are somewhere in between these two extremes.

The important thing to remember is that anyone can accomplish something worthwhile by making a commitment to working out consistently and eating well. Whether you are genetically gifted or just average, what matters most at the end of the day is that you can see your progress in the mirror and feel it in terms of increased strength and vitality.

WHY COMPETE?

A question everyone interested in bodybuilding should ask themselves is, 'What is the point of entering bodybuilding competitions?' For the top professionals the motivation is easy to see. They can earn considerable amounts in prize money and can make a lucrative career if they fully develop their genetic potential. 'Mr Universe' and 'Miss Olympia' winners become sought after as trainers and consultants, get invited to give training and nutrition seminars, own their own gyms, set up mail-order businesses, and earn from product endorsement and advertising just as top stars in other sports do. Those who combine great personal charisma with super bodies become role models for thousands, or, in the exceptional case of someone like the great Arnold Schwarzenegger, for millions of people. These top stars of bodybuilding are a mere handful of the millions of people taking part in the sport and the kind of success they achieve is something that millions can only

Side angle shot showing the extremely small waist of Brian Buchanan, one of the best V shapes ever, at the NABBA Mr Universe competition (1983).

Men's Professional NABBA Mr Universe final. Ed Kawak won the day, beating the likes of Dreyer and Richardson (1983).

dream about. Bodybuilding is far from being unique in this respect. Look at any sport and the top competitors usually stand out because they have special abilities, in part, abilities that they have honed and developed through training, but the genetic potential had to be there in the first place. Consider the super strength of the great Russian weightlifter Vasily Alexeev, the sheer athleticism of Daley Thomson or Carl Lewis. Look at George Foreman's punching power, and the speed, ferocity and accuracy of Mike Tyson, the coordination and agility, not to mention sheer physical size of basketball's Michael Jordan and 'Magic' Johnson. All of these men were genetically gifted to excel at what they do from the start. How far would Mike Tyson have gone as a basketball player or George Foreman as a marathon runner? What kind of weightlifter would 'Magic' Johnson have made? How many baskets would Alexeev have scored had he decided he wanted to be a basketball player? Even Daley Thomson, the best all-round athlete in the world, would only have been a less-than-average shot-putter or discus thrower. Even if he had dedicated all of his energies to either of those events, not through lack of talent or determination, he simply would never have been big enough to compete with the massive strength and leverage advantages of the giants who dominate those sports. As certain old-time coaches used to say, 'You can't put in what God has left out!'

Bodybuilding is no different. Anyone can improve, but great champions are born with a special potential to excel in a given sphere or field. Those who discover where their talents lie when they are fairly young are the lucky ones. In fact, bodybuilding has something in common with martial arts. Quite often the kind of people who take it up are those who are least genetically well endowed to excel in the activity. For a long time, before bodybuilding became massively popular, the number of naturally well-built, muscular individuals, true mesomorphs that took up bodybuilding, was very low. It is an activity which tends to appeal more to those who feel that they are too fat or too skinny and want to look more muscular. The naturally muscular-looking mesomorph is usually happy with the way his body looks and will normally tend to orientate to more performance-oriented sports, perhaps later turning to weight training to increase strength so as to enhance performance in competition against other mesomorphs.

Nowadays more and more mesomorphs are coming into the sport as its status continues to rise. Naturally, the standards rise also.

DANGERS

It is very important to keep a sense of perspective where bodybuilding is concerned. Practised properly, it should be a life-enhancing activity, something that makes you feel better physically and psychologically, a sport or hobby that enriches your lifestyle. Some people become obsessed with the idea of becoming champions to the extent that it takes over, indeed, becomes their life. There are big dangers inherent in this kind of obsessiveness and at least three possible, unfortunate consequences: you become a bodybuilding bum, a bodybuilding bore or a bodybuilding burn out.

Bearing all of this in mind you, naturally end up asking yourself the question, 'Why bother to compete at all, if the chances of going all the way are so remote?' The point is that 'going all the way' is not the only journey. Go as far as you can and you will find it a rewarding experience. The point of competition is, of course, to bring out the best in you, not to win at all costs. Being obsessed with winning and being number one is unhealthy and will ultimately lead to disappointment and frustration. Being determined to get into the best possible shape that you can is not; it is a personal challenge that tests your self-discipline, your determination and your ability to focus your efforts. Winning is something we are all conditioned to desire from childhood, but really the important thing where competition is concerned is the process. You learn a lot about yourself and the way that your body responds to dieting and exercise every time that you compete. Like everything else in life, contest or competition is something that you get better at the more you do it. If you do manage to win or place highly in a competition, the sense of achievement and feelings of success can be extremely gratifying and well worth the blood sweat and tears. If you do not, at least you will have gained some valuable experience of physical conditioning and contest preparation.

If you are intelligent in your approach, write everything down and keep a record of your progress and you will learn what works for you and what does not. If you make mistakes with your diet or training, it will be on record and you can learn from the experience. Competition should be a learning experience and at the end of the day should leave you feeling satisfied and pleased with yourself, as long as the goals that you set yourself are realistic ones in the first place. Always remember that if you do not do as well as you had expected to, it is not the end of the world. There will always be further competitions.

GOALS

Goals are important in bodybuilding and can be divided into short-term goals and long-term goals. The beginner tends to have less clearly defined goals than the intermediate or advanced bodybuilder. If asked what they are trying to achieve, they often reply that they want bigger arms, or better abdominals or even that they want to bench press 300lb. There are all sorts of people who work out and they differ as much in their motivation and goal orientation as they do in their occupations and ages. Some trainees, especially teenagers, start out inspired by what they have read in the magazines and are convinced that the only thing that matters is to become a bodybuilding champion. Some of these are obsessed with proving their manhood and see bodybuilding as the way to do it and go all out to put on muscle, with varying degrees of success. Many beginners who start weight training, while they train almost exclusively to improve their physiques, and do little serious fitness or power training, do not consider themselves to be bodybuilders. Most have no desire to put on a pair of posing trunks and stand up in front of crowds of people to have their physique judged, especially when they themselves are far from happy with the way they look. After a couple of years of going to gyms and training, they often begin to see things differently and unless they are involved in some other sport, can begin to turn seriously towards bodybuilding. Getting up on stage in front of hundreds of people to display your physique is not for the faint hearted though.

GOVERNING BODIES

Bodybuilding is not an Olympic sport and there are various organizations in charge of running and developing it in the English-speaking world. The sport has its amateur and professional ranks and championships are organized at club, district, area, national and international levels. The most prestigious, from the professional bodybuilding point of view, is the 'Mr Olympia' organized by the International Federation of Body Building (IFBB). The English branch of the IFBB is the English Federation of Body Builders or EFBB, and is the main organization in Great Britain. The National Amateur Body Building Association is also very active. NABBA is actually an international organization and the standard of its top competitors is world class. Bodybuilding is making huge strides in other countries too and an interesting development which has taken place recently is the formation of the Australian Natural Body Building Federation. Competitors must take random drug tests and prove they have not taken any steroids in the last five years by taking a polygraph lie detector test.

DRUGS IN COMPETITIVE BODYBUILDING

One of the great problems with bodybuilding as a sport is the use or abuse of drugs, in particular anabolic steroids. Abuse occurs even at the club level among people who have no intention of competing and it is rife among competitors at high level. There is little or no testing and many people feel that it is impossible to win without taking them. Bodybuilding as a sport has been hypocritical and operated with double standard. It has been guilty of sending out mixed messages about drug taking. It is common knowledge that anabolic steroids, human growth hormone and other chemical aids do work.

Tim Belknap (USA) winning his height class at NABBA Amateur Mr Universe (1983).

Anabolic steroids were originally developed to assist returning prisoners of war emaciated by malnutrition from life in concentration camps to recover their strength. Basically, they allow for faster, more effective recuperation and drastically increase the speed at which muscles grow. They do, however, have a number of unpleasant harmful side effects. Prolonged steroid abuse has undoubtedly been directly responsible for the deaths of a number of bodybuilders. The governments of both Great Britain and the USA have made anabolic steroids a category A drug. Dealing in them, possession of them or taking them is a criminal offence.

As with most substance abuse-related crimes the people who take them do so because they want to. This is really at the heart of the problem. Show organizers have tended not to impose drug tests because when tests have been announced, the standard of the shows has dropped dramatically along with the attendance of the paying public who want to see the maximum possible size and muscularity, which so far can only be achieved by taking these drugs. The fact that the law has now outlawed steroids should mean that their use will decline. This would be the best thing that could possibly happen to bodybuilding. If nobody took them, nobody would feel the need to take them in order to compete. In that way competition would be both fairer and safer. At the end of the day, taking steroids to win a competition will be just another form of cheating, not something athletes feel compelled to do to have a chance of winning.

A FIVE-YEAR PLAN FOR COMPETITION

A serious beginning bodybuilder, if blessed with good genetics, may have the long-term goal of becoming a national champion within five years. This would basically involve training heavy and aiming to grow, with occasional dieting and peaking for less important contests along the way. Often to qualify for a national championships, it is necessary to place at regional or area level, so these lesser contests (while not the ultimate goal), must be taken seriously and prepared for diligently if the aim is to qualify for the nationals. If the national title was your goal, basically you have five years in which to prepare by training heavy and eating well. Anyone gaining 5 to 6lb (2.3 to 2.7kg) of muscle in a year, training and eating naturally, without using anabolic steroids, testosterone, growth hormone or any of the other potentially dangerous chemical substances would be well advised to be delighted with their progress. An increase in muscular mass of 25 to 30lb (11 to 14kg) over five years makes an enormous difference to a physique. Think how many lean beef steaks you would have to pile on a plate for there to be 25 to 30lb of meat and you get some idea. Five pounds a year does not sound like a lot but look at 5lb (2.3kg) of meat on a plate and you realize just how much tissue growth is involved.

Teenagers aged sixteen and over can make astounding gains because the body is still secreting natural growth hormone and so it responds readily to the direct stimulation placed on the muscles by high-intensity training. Generally the older the bodybuilder is, the harder it becomes to gain muscle. However, it is almost always possible to improve. Assuming that the trainee bodybuilder intends to enter one important contest a year, the following are some of the points consider along the way.

In many cases diet is more crucial than type, frequency or duration of training sessions, and is often the real culprit when people seem to stop making progress. There are various complaints about diet of the following sort: 'I do not gain any muscle'. 'I cannot get defined (I am still fat)'. 'When I try to get defined, I lose muscle size as well as fat.' Although sometimes incorrect training methods can be a factor, more often than not, a bad diet is the cause of the problem.

COUNTDOWN TO COMPETITION

Once a certain amount of progress has been made the bodybuilder has at some point to take the plunge and decide to compete – or not. Once a reasonable amount of muscular size has been gained you pick a competition and aim to get into top form for it. There now follows a four-month completely drug-free plan, describing how to get into contest shape. This involves speeding up the metabolism, modifying the diet and training in order to burn off the last vestiges of body fat so as to be able to compete in highly defined muscular condition. Let us first just recap on the nutritional needs of the body.

Nutrition

As a rule of thumb, you need about a gram of protein to maintain each pound of muscular bodyweight. So a 180lb (82kg) bodybuilder needs to consume 6oz (180g) of protein to ensure that there is enough protein available for muscles to grow. One gram of protein can be achieved from every four calories consumed if we consider foods such as chicken, fish, eggs or meat. That amounts to 720 calories. Now if we bear in mind that the body needs fifteen calories per pound of body weight for the same body weight to be maintained, assuming moderate activity the bodybuilder with 10 to 15 per cent body-fat levels (generally accepted as healthy levels) can consume up to 2,700 calories a day. Now on a strict diet designed to get body-fat levels down to 4 or 5 per cent, the bodybuilder has to cut calorie consumption, but not at the expense of protein intake. This has to be kept up to ensure muscle growth or at the very least no muscle loss. By reducing the calorie intake to 2,000 a day, fat loss is guaranteed. Assuming an allowance of 10 per cent fat in the diet (200 calories) and with 760 taken up by protein ingestion that leaves 1,080 calories that can be made up from carbohydrates. When dieting for competition, it is important to select your carbohydrates carefully and to vary them as much as possible. That way you can cut the boredom out of your diet and make your bodybuilding lifestyle more varied and compatible with those around you who may not share your enthusiasm for discipline and calorie counting when the time comes to sit down to eat.

Contest preparation with hard intense training sessions and strict dieting is psychologically very hard for some people. They feel that they are denying themselves and making sacrifices, and sometimes become irritable and get into bad moods. This is especially so when they go in for carbohydrate depletion in the final week of contest preparation. This is negative thinking and should be avoided. You are entering the contest because *you* have chosen to. It is not your family's fault or anyone else's that you cannot have an icecream or a cream cake when they can eat whatever they feel like. If life seems hard and unfair as a consequence, do no inflict your sense of how hard or unjust it is on them. It is not their fault, responsibility or problem. It is your decision to deny yourself. Feel good about how disciplined you are and visualize how great you

are going to look on the day of the contest. That way you make it easier on yourself and the people you love.

If you are serious about competing and want to come in in the best possible form, you should start 'cleaning up' your diet four months before the competition date. The following procedures should be observed.

- Cut back on fats and remove red meat from your diet.
- Step your aerobic exercise up to 20 minutes a day, six days a week for the first month. In the second month, increase your aerobic training to 30 minutes and in the third month increase to 45 minutes a day, six days a week. Keep your pulse rate at the 60 per cent of maximum range to avoid the risk of burning off muscle.
- Vary your aerobic training. Try a mixture of exercise bike, rowing machine, treadmill, swimming, skipping, walking, or any similar activity to add some variety and avoid boredom.
- The last month, which is really only three weeks should see an increase in aerobic activity to 45 minutes a day, seven days a week or an hour a day split into two 30-minute sessions. My personal preference was always to do stationary bike in the morning for 30 minutes and then after my evening workout, I would do 30 minutes on the treadmill.

Eat six small meals a day rather than three larger ones. This keeps your metabolism higher and assists in burning body fat as well as ensuring a constant steady supply of nutrients is available when you need it. People with slow metabolisms should take digestive enzyme tablets before each meal to help speed up the digestive process and ensure rapid, effective recuperation from the effects of exercise.

Water is vital to the body, especially when it is under the stress of heavy training. The amount of aerobics being done to get into contest shape means that you will sweat and lose a lot of moisture, so you should drink at least 5 pints (3 litres) of water a day, preferably at regular intervals in small quantities. Supplementation helps when you place your body under the kind of stress you do when training and dieting for a contest. Take 3g of vitamin C per day, a good multivitamin tablet, a mineral tablet and one to three B-complex tablets. If you can afford them, amino acids are a very desirable addition to your diet.

Bodybuilding Workout Routine

First Month

In the first month, you work out four days a week doing a four-day split, weight training Monday and Tuesday, resting Wednesday (apart from half-an-hour's aerobics) and weight training Thursday and Friday.

It is advisable to train with the maximum possible intensity, without getting injured, so always stretch and warm-up thoroughly. Concentrate on basic bread-and-butter exercises. Do a first warm up set of fifteen repetitions and then aim to work in the range of eight to twelve repetitions per set, increasing the weight on each set.

Chest: a typical chest workout might include bench press, incline bench press and dips, and the aim would be to handle the maximum weight possible for each set. The exercises would be done like this. Bench press: first set – fifteen reps to warm up. Four minutes' rest then a set of twelve repetitions with the maximum weight you can handle without partner assistance. Rest four minutes and aim to do ten reps with the maximum weight you can for the third set.

Rest for four to five minutes and increase the weight again to the maximum that you can manage for eight reps for the fourth set. Move on to incline bench press and follow the same pattern. Finish off with dips. The total work done for chest would amount to twelve high-intensity sets.

Follow the same model for these other body parts.

Triceps: select three basic exercises from: close-grip bench, push-downs, French press, bench dips with hands close together, etc.
Shoulders: select three basic exercises from: seated dumb-bell press, press behind neck, military press, upright rowing, Arnold press, etc.
Quadriceps: select three basic exercises from squat, leg-press, leg-extensions, front squat, hack squat, etc.
Calves: select three basic exercises from: standing calf-raises, seated calf-raises, donkey-raises, toe press, etc.
Leg biceps: select two basic exercises, for example, leg curls and stiff-legged deadlifts.
Trapezius: select two basic exercises from barbell or dumb-bell shrugs, upright rowing, etc.
Biceps: select two basic exercises from barbell curl, preacher curl, seated inclined dumb-bells, etc. The biceps is a small two-headed muscle and often gets overtrained. Bear in mind it also works fairly hard, even though only indirectly, in many of the back exercises.
Back: select three basic exercises from pullovers, deadlifts, chins, seated rows, pull-downs, bent-over rowing, etc. The back is such a large area of interconnected muscles it responds well to variety. Also the weak link in back training tends to be the arms. A good training strategy is to pre-exhaust back first with four sets of straight-arm pull-overs. This leaves the arms reasonably fresh for the heavy work. The grip can be another weak link, in which case use powerlifting straps.

Abdominals: select three exercises from inclined sit-ups, Roman chair sit-ups, hanging leg-raises, inclined leg-raises, twists and crunches. Do three sets of fifteen to twenty every day. Do abdominals more slowly than any other exercise. Doing them slowly really makes them burn, gives you a better feeling and a fantastic looking midsection.

This training routine gives you the perfect combination of intensity and variety. The combination of sets and rest times is the key to maximum growth for exercise. Go for maximum intensity and then allow for sufficient recovery in your actual workouts.

Second Month

In the second month, change the frequency of workouts to five times a week if your gym closes on Sundays. If it is open seven days a week train one day, rest one day (but still do 30 minutes of aerobics on rest days at 60–70 per cent maximum heart rate). Cut the rest period between sets to 3 minutes except for heavy leg workouts where you can take up to 5 minutes.

Third Month

In the third month, train one day on and one day off, doing two 30-minute aerobics sessions or one 45-minute aerobics session on your off days.

Cut the rest time between sets down to 2½ minutes and keep the reps in the ten to fifteen range.

Final Month

In the last three weeks leading up to the contest week, train one day on and one day off,

doing two 45-minute aerobic sessions on the off days if you are not lean enough and still need to burn more fat. If your definition is on target, cut back to two 30-minute aerobic sessions. Keep practising your posing routine every day, moving fluidly from pose to pose.

Add some additional exercises to your workouts such as flys for chest, lunges for legs, bent-over lateral-raises for shoulders, concentration curls for biceps, kickbacks for triceps, back-raises for lower back, and so on.

Last Fortnight

In the last week before the week of the contest, train every day and keep reps in the ten to fifteen range. Include supersetting on the final exercise of each group.

Contest Week

Cut your carbohydrate intake by one half. So if it was 1,300 calories a day, reduce it to 650 calories. Your carbohydrate intake will stay at that level for Sunday, Monday and Tuesday. The 650-calorie deficit must be made up by consuming more protein and a little fat; not replacing these calories will result in muscle loss. Workouts during these three days should include more sets, fifteen as opposed to twelve and higher reps in the fifteen to twenty range. This will help accelerate the burning of stored carbohydrates and glycogen in the muscles. My last leg workout has always been some eight days before the contest as I felt that my legs stayed gorged with blood and looked less defined if I trained them any closer to contest day. This preparation always allowed me to come in with much better separation and striations.

167

Last Three Days

Wednesday and Thursday should be the days of highest carbohydrate consumption or loading. Increase your carbohydrate intake to double the normal amount so if you had cut back from 1,300 to 650, now you go up to 2,600 carbohydrate-rich calories. On the Friday if you are looking full and ready to compete then ease off on the carbohydrate so that you can maintain your condition. If by any chance you look flat, then continue carbohydrate loading as on Wednesday and Thursday. If you have over-loaded on carbohydrates which is unlikely but sometimes happens, you know on Friday, which gives you twenty-four hours to cut back as necessary on the carbohydrates and make adjustments to come in looking ripped on the day.

This method of carbohydrate loading is tried and tested and will help you to come in looking your best, unlike the last-minute attempts at carbohydrate loading which all too often end in disaster. I always used it to come in looking full, ripped and cut.

Water and Salt

On Sunday, Monday and Tuesday, do not add any salt whatsoever to your food and drink water freely. *Do not, repeat, do not under any circumstances stop drinking water!* On Wednesday and Thursday, drink normally. On Friday, drink only small amounts whenever you feel thirsty.

OTHER CONTEST-PREPARATION TIPS

Posing

Whatever shape you get your body into, it is vitally important that you practise posing. Practice makes perfect. Good posing can make

Checking posing and condition.

a big difference to final placings in a contest and anyone who enters without preparing their posing routine adequately will lose out.

The first poses to practise are the seven or eight compulsory poses (depending on the bodybuilding authority). These comprise:

Abdominals and thighs.

Front double biceps.

- Abdominals and thighs
- Front lat spread
- Double biceps
- Side chest
- Side triceps

- Rear lat spread, showing calf and thigh biceps
- Rear double biceps
- Most muscular (compulsory in NABBA but not in IFBB shows)

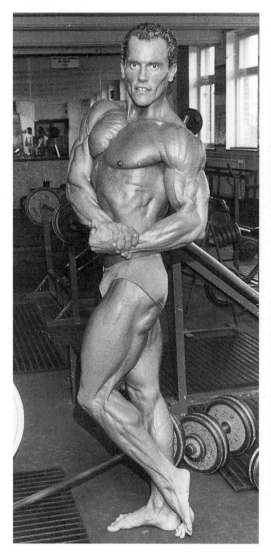

Side chest shot showing maximum definition and good proportions.

Side triceps shot.

Women bodybuilders do the same compulsory poses with the exception of the 'most muscular'. The judges are looking for specific, concrete features in each of these poses.

- In the abdominals and thighs pose, there

should be visible separation and striations of the quadriceps. Any fat obscuring the abdominals, serratus or intercostals is considered a serious defect.
- In the front lat spread, the judges are looking for a wide symmetrical back and a

Back lat spread: still room for improvement.

Back double biceps.

narrow waist, but do not forget your shoulders, arms and, something a lot of people fall down on, the positioning of the legs.

- In the double biceps, try to show a big arm, thick triceps but above all, a big well-shaped biceps with a high peak and separation. Check the difference that slightly angling the forearm and wrists makes to the biceps appearance.

- In side chest, the essential point is pectoral development and thickness, but do not forget the legs and arms. A good arch of the ribcage helps, and remember to keep the shoulder farthest away high, to lift the far side of the chest.

- A good side triceps pose will show a nice horseshoe effect, fullness and horizontal striations.
- The full rear lat spread with leg biceps and calf should emphasize width and flare of the back, but the arms should be positioned to give a pleasing symmetrical effect. Do not forget to show both legs to good effect when demonstrating the leg biceps and calf. Any fat in the lower back area is a weak point.
- The rear double biceps is all about showing arms and shoulders to their best advantage. The judges are looking for full separated peaked biceps, full separated triceps, and will want to see all three heads of the deltoids.
- The most muscular is just what the name says. It shows the judges everything. Do not forget to tense the legs as well as the upper body and abdomen.

As well as harmonious symmetrical development, the judges will be looking carefully at size, shape, muscle quality, definition, proportion and good posture and deportment. Depending on the nature and type of competition that you have entered, you will have the opportunity to do free posing to your own selection of music. If you reach the finals, you will have to pose-down against other competitors, which is where the time you have spent posing and studying the opposition's strengths and weaknesses really pays off.

Great champions are usually superb posers and their routines resemble a sort of muscular ballet done to music that flows from one pose to another.

Posing Tips

- Use the same mirror to check your visual aspect every day at the same time. First thing in the morning is when you look most defined, because of water loss through perspiration while sleeping.
- Check your compulsory poses in front of a mirror. First do them with your eyes closed, then check them by opening your eyes to make sure that your positioning is correct.
- Listen to your posing music daily. Learn every beat.
- Make three copies of posing music. Tapes can easily be lost or damaged and the last thing you need on the day of a contest is to be running around trying to get a copy of your favourite tape!
- Have your posing routine worked out four months before the competition and practise running through it without tensing three times a day.
- In the final week practise your posing routine ten times a day. Practise flowing from one pose into another without tensing the muscles hard the first nine times. The tenth time, practise flexing and tensing all the muscles.

Tanning

If you can afford to, you can start using a sunbed two months before the date of the competition. This will give you a base tan and will help the effect of the tanning cream applied in the last week. Half an hour, two to three times a week will be sufficient. Make sure to spend your time on the sunbed in different positions to ensure that you get an even, all-over tan. Today there are many good tanning products on the market and if applied correctly over the last three days, any white bodybuilder can come in with a dark, even tan. Remember that stage lights are

Front lat spread: the 80kg class at the 1986 British Finals.

very bright and an average tan alongside dark tans and black bodybuilders will make you appear pallid and white and will not show your muscularity and definition to your best advantage.

Competition Day

On the day of the competition, try to stay relaxed and most importantly have all your arrangements made and everything organized in advance, so that all goes smoothly. Ideally, you will be staying in a hotel near the venue, your travelling arrangements will be taken care of, and your friends, training partners, supporters and rivals will be there to share the day with you. You have trained your best, dieted strictly and you have come to compete in your best possible shape. You have perfected your posing routine and you are waiting to show the crowd the results of all your hard work.

Try not to be nervous. It is only one day out of your life. An important one. One that you have worked hard for and one that you deserve to enjoy to the full. So be yourself. Go for it. Show them what you have got. Above all, enjoy it!

7 Safety, Injury and Rehabilitation

GYM DISCIPLINE

Most of the safety procedures that should be followed in the gym are basic common sense and have been covered in Chapter 2. Just to recap, the following guidelines should always be kept in mind.

- Always warm-up properly.
- Remember to stretch regularly.
- Use collars to make sure weights cannot slide off bars.
- Always ensure there is a spotter or spotters on hand when heavy weights are being handled.
- Use a weightlifting belt for lower back and abdominal support, especially when handling heavy weights, squatting, deadlifting or lifting overhead.
- Avoid doing ballistic movements as this magnifies stress on joints, ligaments and muscles.
- Always observe correct exercise form and aim to develop a balanced, symmetrical physique.
- Do all exercises with a weight that you can handle safely and aim for steady, not spectacular progress. If you persistently train with weights that are too heavy for you to perform the exercises with correct form you will, sooner or later, injure yourself.
- Avoid overtraining. There are two kinds of overtraining, excessive intensity and excessive frequency. Excessive intensity will lead to torn muscles, ligaments or tendons and

frequent overtraining will lead to bursitis, tendinitis, pulled muscles and sore joints.

INJURIES

What Do They Consist Of?

Human nature and physiology being what they are, hardly anyone who trains never gets injured. Many of the commonest training injuries are relatively trivial and easily dealt with; others can be quite serious and cause long-term problems. The most common problems tend to be pulled muscles, strained ligaments and tendons, headaches, burst blood vessels and haemorrhoids, all of which can vary considerably in severity. Less common, but generally more serious are dislocations, hernias and ruptures. Following the procedures outlined above is the best way to avoid these problems, but if you do get injured, you should know what the injury consists of.

Muscle Injuries

The muscles are tissues composed of bundles of fibres capable of contracting to generate force. The thickness, composition and architecture of muscle fibres varies considerably in different parts of the body, but all muscles are prone to slight tears if suddenly overloaded. Impact damage may be caused by bouncing a bar off the chest in bench press or similar exercises. Damage caused may be intermuscular or intramuscular, the latter being more serious and taking longer to heal as it occurs deep within the muscle fibres, not just between them.

Muscle fibres do not regenerate, but are repaired by the formation of scar tissue, which weakens the muscle and forms palpable nodules. Muscle injuries must have rest for recovery to take place. In the first 48 hours, muscle damage cannot be massaged or stretched away, trained off, sprayed or injected away. Attempting any of these procedures can lead to a weakening of the scar tissue, cyst formation or haematoma, myositis ossificans (when the haematoma is transformed into a bony lump) which can seriously impair future progress, and scar-tissue adhesion to other muscles, tendons or bones resulting in a loss of mobility and the capacity for full extension. An immediate application of an ice pack is the best treatment. All good gyms should have a refrigerator with ice available.

Fortunately, the muscles are well supplied with blood which transports oxygen and promotes rapid healing. After the initial 48-hour rest period, it is important to get the injured muscle back into movement as muscle which is unused atrophies rapidly. Correct recovery involves gentle movements and a combination of static, active and passive muscle exercises to restore full functionality. You should return to exercising the damaged muscles gradually. Never rush back to full activity as you will almost certainly aggravate the injury.

The severity of muscle sprains and pulls can vary considerably. Slight tears in the thin sheets of muscles in the erector spinae muscles of the lower back recover in a matter of days with the correct combination of rest and gentle exercise; torn pectorals, biceps and rotator cuff muscles, however, can take much longer to heal. In some cases the damage may be permanent, particularly when caused by very heavy weights.

When a muscle injury is noted, training should be halted and ice applied immediately. Ice applied at ten minute intervals in the first half hour to two hours of the injury happening is the only real treatment. The cold causes blood vessels to constrict and reduces swelling and pain.

Tendons

Tendons are hard, non-elastic strips or straps of fibrous tissue which join muscles to bones. They do not contract as muscles do and are extremely strong – the Achilles tendon can support a load of half a ton per square inch. They do not usually snap, but can be sprained by being stretched into an abnormal position. This is accompanied by various degrees of swelling depending upon whether there is a tendon sheath involved; if there is the swelling extends above the sheath and is more obvious. Treatment is 24 hours complete rest, ice, compression (in the shape of a crepe bandage or elastic support of some kind and elevation. Depending upon how bad the injury is, normal function may not return for one to two weeks.

A partially ruptured tendon is more serious and will generally require rest and support for two to six weeks, as well as physiotherapy. Tendons can be completely ruptured (pulled away from the bone) in a serious case. Typical sites for this type of injury are the Achilles, the shoulder cuff and the long head of the biceps. If this kind of injury occurs in the upper leg, when squatting, it is normally accompanied by a severe dislocation. Complete rupture normally requires surgical suture and six to eight weeks immobilization, and total rest. Any damage takes considerably longer to repair than in a muscle, as the blood supply is vastly inferior.

175

Ligaments

Ligaments are strands of solid, fibrous connective tissue which join together two or more bones or cartilages, or support a muscle, muscle sheath or organ. They are similar to tendons in composition and recovery characteristics. A sprained ligament can recover within a week, a rupture requires surgery and up to ten weeks for total recovery to take place. Apart from the treatments mentioned, any other remedies should be medically prescribed. Hydrocortisone (steroid) injections should only ever be given by a doctor. Those who believe in self-medication should understand that a little knowledge is a dangerous thing. Cortisone injections are sometimes given for partial ruptures of ligaments, but in the case of a partial rupture of a tendon, they will result in a complete rupture by interfering with the blood supply and weakening the collagen structure.

The symptoms of injuries are tearing, or snapping sensations, pain, swelling, bruising, prolonged burning and restricted mobility. Under no circumstances should you suffer in silence. Medical assistance should be sought whenever necessary.

The above injuries could be described as intensity injuries. Less dramatic, but just as debilitating if not treated, are overuse injuries which manifest themselves in aching joints and inflammation around tendons. Wrists, elbows, shoulders and knees are the most common sites of pain of this kind which is usually either bursitis, tenosynovitis or peritendinitis. Longer rests between training sessions, lighter weights, bandages for joint support and altering exercise technique should be tried first. Warming-up should involve plenty of light flushing movements to promote good blood supply to the affected areas. If pain persists, consult a doctor who will probably recommend rest, steroid injections, ultrasound or general physiotherapy as possible alternative treatments.

Exercises Commonly Associated with Injuries

The bench press, dumb-bell flys, squats, deadlift, power cleans, snatch, and cheating curls are not inherently dangerous if performed correctly with an appropriate amount of weight. However, they frequently result in injury when sloppy technique is combined with heavy weights. Prevention is better than cure, so be aware of the dangers!

Pylometrics are explosive jumping-type exercises designed to develop explosive power. They are undoubtedly effective but need specialized preparation because of the stresses they place on joints and connective tissue.

The cheating technique is intended to increase the intensity of the exercise but it can cause injuries. Take the case of cheating curls. The exercise is intended to be for the biceps, but frequently the much stronger leg and back muscles are used to heave the weight most of the way up. Then a manic attempt to finish the movement with a rapid contraction of the biceps is made, which may be likely to cause tiny muscle tears. Other problems associated with this exercise include lower back strains which result from doing the movement almost like a reverse clean.

Trying to resist the descent of a weight that is actually far too heavy for you is potentially equally dangerous. A good example would be attempting negatives in bench press and squat. Ballistic movements are potentially injurious in all exercises.

These are some of the reasons that throughout this book, we have stressed the importance of correct exercise form. You only have one body – look after it.

Recuperation

Injury treatment is vitally important if full and lasting recovery is to be achieved. In most sports, when an injury occurs, the normal formula for treatment is described by the acronym RICE. This stands for Rest, Ice, Compression and Elevation. This formula should always be remembered.

In the context of bodybuilding, if an injury occurs, 'rest' means stop exercising immediately. Do not attempt to finish the set or go on to a different body part. It also means giving your body time to heal. Do not rush back into the gym as you are almost certain to re-injure the affected area if it has not had time to heal.

Injuries are generally a negative experience, but they do allow time for you to rest and reflect on your training methods, progress and future goals. Inevitably you will learn more about anatomy and how your body works.

Rehabilitation

Professional help and advice is always available if you want it. There is a variety of methods and techniques which are more or less suitable for different kinds of injury. Seventy-two hours after the initial trauma has been treated by ice, heat can be an effective treatment for relieving pain and tension. Alternate hot and cold can be particularly good for reducing the dangers of calcification.

Physiotherapy and massage are generally well known and popular forms of treatment for many kinds of injury. Less well known but just as effective, sometimes more so, are the kind of manipulation techniques offered by osteopaths and chiropractors. Massage, in particular, is excellent for general wellbeing and for getting rid of unwanted muscular stiffness, tension and associated aches and pains, and if used sensibly can help avoid injuries happening in the first place. Many types of muscular soreness and muscle spasm-related pain can be alleviated by massage, although it cannot repair muscle damage. Again, it is often a case of finding the right kind of massage for your particular problem. Shiatsu is especially good for certain kinds of lower back pain.

Drugs

Bodybuilding, if done correctly is actually not a particularly dangerous sport and many of its practitioners go on training into a ripe old age, enjoying the benefits earned from a lifetime's training. The key phrase in this statement is 'if done correctly'. Almost any sport can result in injuries if the practitioner does not follow basic safety guidelines and procedures. In some sports, like climbing, skiing, boxing, rugby, horse-riding and sub-aqua diving, to pick just a random selection, ignorance, carelessness or recklessness can have fatal consequences. Deaths associated with bodybuilding are thankfully very rare. One danger is the risk of illness caused by drug abuse.

Drug-taking is, unfortunately, endemic in many sports and bodybuilding is no exception. However, in most sports, drug-taking to gain or recover an advantage over an opponent usually only occurs at the highest levels, where important titles and very often big money is at stake. Bodybuilding is unfortunate in the respect that even relative beginners have been known to get into drug-taking. The main culprits are the anabolic steroids, which many people see as the solution to their difficulties in gaining muscle. There is no doubt that these drugs do work, but there are all sorts of complications, side effects and consequences that must be taken into account. They can cause liver failure, sterility, impotence and a host of other health problems.

Anabolic steroids are not the only controversial substances taken in the pursuit of bigger, leaner, more muscular bodies. So are testosterone, insulin and human growth hormone. What makes all of these substances considerably more dangerous is that they are provided and administered by people who are not doctors and have little grasp of the dangers involved. There have even been cases where more experienced users have put novices on a course, just to see what the results are, using them as guinea pigs for experiments of their own. The only safe procedure where these kinds of drugs are concerned is not to take them. They are illegal as well as dangerous, and in the long term no good will come from taking them.

Main muscle groups of Dennis Oakes. (Above) side triceps; (right) back.

8 Bodybuilding: Personal Views

BODYBUILDING AS A LIFESTYLE

Dennis Oakes

As a youngster I was always involved in sports and physical activities. Growing up in the East End of London where it could get pretty rough at times, physical toughness was important. I tried my hand at a few sports with the intention of making myself tougher. I did judo a couple of times, karate for a while and in the best East End tradition, boxing. My father was keen for me to be involved in sport, and had been a keen amateur boxer himself, but when I came home one day with my face in a real mess after a tough bout (which I had actually won), my mother put her foot down and that was the end of my boxing career. In a way it was a bit of a relief, because boxing is a really tough and demanding sport. I was fairly short for my weight and I often found myself facing taller boys with a much longer reach, and although I could usually get inside eventually, I used to take some real hidings in the course of getting inside their defences.

When I left school, I began to work in the Smithfield meat market which was a real eye opener. There were some real characters working there, some real tough, hard men, ex-World and Commonwealth boxing champions, like Terry McGovern and karate experts like Terry Stewart and some immensely strong, genetically gifted individuals. I was impressed by physical strength, men who could run while carrying two hundredweight of beef on their shoulders or pushing barrows an average man could hardly move.

I wanted to be able to stand up for myself and be respected too. So I began training in an old-style gym at Barking Weightlifting Club, run by Ron Francis, one of the old-time lifters. The men training there were what I call 'beef stews' and 'pints of milk men'. They trained long and hard with heavy weights and ate big, protein-laden meals. They would no sooner have taken anabolic steroids than heroin or any other drug. Natural training was the order of the day and it was effective. As my love for the sport grew, so did the urge to work out in other gyms. In the 1970s in England everyone was either a member of the IFBB as was or NABBA. I would go as often as I could to see Oscar Heidenstam, who was the president of NABBA, a real gentleman and the editor of *Health and Strength* magazine. Oscar was a much loved and respected member of the bodybuilding community and a lovely man. He would always stop work to have a friendly encouraging chat and I used to leave his office with a bundle of back issues of *Health and Strength* and all the motivation in the world.

I often travelled to Wag Bennett's Gym in London, where Wag and his wife Diane, two of the greats of British bodybuilding, were always on hand to have a chat about their friends in bodybuilding and give advice on training, diet and such like. In the early 1980s,

Kneeling side triceps.

the first Weider shop in Great Britain opened in central London. I used to travel there every week to keep up to date with developments on the bodybuilding scene and chat to the manager, at the time a fantastic young bodybuilder called Martin Alamangos, who was later to become British champion and turn professional. The Weider shop became a meeting place for bodybuilders, and was frequented by enthusiasts and champions alike.

I remember the first time I saw the veteran IFBB star Albert Beccles there. He was wearing a big woolly cardigan and it looked as if he had something stuffed up his sleeves. It turned out to be his biceps! I had never seen a man with such big arms; they completely blew my mind at the time. I frequently used to chat to a photographer called Dudley Carver who used to go to all the contests and photograph the up-and-coming new faces. He was always praising different ones, predicting that they would be future champions. Just for a bit of fun I would tease him by saying things like 'No abs, weak chest, no legs' or something of that sort. One day he came up to me with a wild gleam in his eye, brandishing some 10 × 8 black-and-white prints and said, 'This time I've got him. He's a real monster; 6 feet tall, 15 stones and he's only been training two years. Look.' For once I was at a loss for words, all I could think of to reply was 'Two years? Are you sure?' The newcomer in the photograph was Dorian Yates. Enough said.

It was at the Weider shop that I met Brian Buchanan who was Junior 'Mr Britain' at the time. His physique just freaked me out. He had recently begun training at a gym called King's Gym and invited me to go and train there too. King's Gym in London was where I really got into the world of bodybuilding. Brian Buchanan helped me a lot with guidance and friendship and there were a lot of serious bodybuilders working out there including the great Wilf Sylvester, 'Mr Britain' and 'Mr Universe'. As well as becoming a many times 'Mr Universe' himself, Brian was in the *Guinness Book of Records* for having the greatest difference between his chest and waist measurements. Genetically gifted and a highly intelligent trainer, he was an awesome sight to behold and an inspiration for any up-and-coming youngster who wanted to be a bodybuilder, like Andrew Croft, Lawrence McCoy, JD, Amory Francis, Trevor Green and a host of others.

I trained for my first contest with Stef Zhichi and, following the advice of Brian Buchanan, entered and won the the South East Britain championships in my class. I trained for the British championships with an irrepressible Welshman named Carl who was as strong as an ox and had a heart of gold. I never did find out his surname, but we had some great workouts together. Brian Buchanan gave me a lot of advice on preparation and support on the day and I won the British intermediate championship that year. I returned from Birmingham to King's Gym a champion, the conquering hero, and the support and congratulations I received from everyone was overwhelming.

I changed jobs about this time and the only time I could train was very early in the morning. I immediately realized that to get the best out of my early morning workouts, I needed a training partner and I was lucky enough to meet a man who was to become a great friend and the best training partner I could have wished for. His name was Laurence McFoy. Laurence had everything, the genetics, desire, courage, determination and self-discipline. We became training partners and best friends. King's Gym was a long way from both our homes and we would both travel across London every morning and meet up to train before work at 5.30am. It was very hard, especially in the cold, dark winter months but our suffering paid off. Laurence competed that

Lawrence McFoy helping Dennis Oakes check out his condition before a show.

John, helped make the day a total success. Many of the best bodybuilders in Great Britain and indeed the world were present that day, including Dorian Yates, Wilf Sylvester, Angie Lester, Selwyn Cotterel and a host of others.

Preparing for the British championships was a long hard process. Training with maximum intensity to stimulate muscle growth and then trying to hold the gains made while dieting for maximum definition requires a lot of discipline, motivation and focus, and a lot of support from your family and loved ones. My diet, in retrospect, seems insane. I virtually lived on chicken and pineapple for three months and as well as my bodybuilding workouts, I spent about an hour a day pedalling at high speed with moderate resistance on a static bicycle. The fashion in the early 1980s was high protein, low carbohydrate and zero fat, which although reasonably effective, was a real test of willpower and even at times of your sanity. Carbohydrate deprivation tends to make you irritable and prone to lose your temper, which makes things difficult for you and your loved ones. Modern bodybuilding diets are a lot healthier and a lot easier to stay on. Happily it all paid off. I got into the shape of my life and won the South West championships at light heavyweight in 1986. I remember a moment that made me feel really special when Dorian Yates, now five times 'Mr Olympia' came up to me and asked in a genuinely interested way what I had been doing to get so cut.

The rest of the year went extremely well too, but one month before competing in what was to be my last British final, disaster struck. It was our day for training legs and Lawrence and I used to train very intensely, shocking the muscles into growth with hard, heavy squatting sessions. I had forgotten my training belt and so I was using one of the belts that belonged to the gym. It was a very old

year while I rested and concentrated on getting bigger. Laurence won everything he entered and I became leaner, bigger and harder. The support we had at every contest was incredible and we both just seemed to go from strength to strength.

With the help of two other British amateur bodybuilders, Stef Zhicci and Sean O'Reilly, we organized the first bodybuilding clinic at World Gym in London. The owners, Ray and belt, dried out with sweat but it seemed serviceable enough. I had about 400lb (180kg) on the bar and was absolutely tuned in to what I was doing. On about the third rep, going down the belt snapped, it just exploded. Luckily for me Lawrence was on hand to catch me and help me back into the rack. He asked me if I was OK and I said that I was and with that he took a belt from another friend and said, 'Well finish your set then'.

I did too, and it was not until later that day when eating a large protein laden meal that I realized I had a serious injury. It turned out that I had ruptured myself in two places, the belly button and higher up the midsection. Lawrence and I talked over what to do about the injury, and how much the contest meant to us both. We decided that I could still compete with a chance of winning if I changed my weight category, trained lighter and ate less. That is exactly what I did. I wore a belt all the time, trained carefully and ate smaller meals. I tried to get my weight down to compete in the middleweight category, but a day before the championships, I was still a kilogram too heavy. So I had to compete as the lightest competitor in the light heavyweight category. The last day was a painful process of eating carbohydrates and praying hard. In the end I came third, which was a good result given the circumstances. A month later, I was operated on and my rupture was fixed, but my midsection was never the same again and that was my last show. Lawrence too was to suffer a terrible injury doing hack squat, rupturing a tendon and dislocating his knee, but years of rehabilitation, hard work and dedication meant he was able to return to competition.

Bodybuilding continues to be important to me, but my goals are different from what they were when I was younger. Being healthy is my first concern and I will do nothing to jeopardize my health, and beyond that I train just to look good. I train hard, watch what I eat and keep myself big and strong with reasonably low levels of body fat. I have little interest now in gaining the kind of muscular bulk of the top professionals whose photographs appear in all the bodybuilding magazines, although I have to admit I occasionally envy them! Too much bulk even in the form of muscle rather than fat, means extra work for the cardiovascular system and the joints, and in long term it is counterproductive. My aim is to keep looking and feeling great by staying big and strong while retaining agility and flexibility and keeping injury-free. I have tuned into my natural biorhythms and am quite happy to gain or lose a few pounds depending upon the time of year, work, holidays, and so on.

Rather than being an obsession for me, bodybuilding now is my way of life. I earn my living as a personal trainer, helping people to solve their physical problems through intelligent exercise routines and informed dietary advice. A personal trainer has a lot to offer and anyone who can afford one would do well to seriously consider the investment. I have seen so many people, who have trained for years without really improving, make good gains just by making relatively small adjustments, or a change of strategy. There are so many confused people working out in gyms and health clubs these days, it is quite amazing. The confusion that exists is a consequence of an over-availability of information, much of it apparently contradictory or of an excessively technical nature. There is also a tendency for people to accept programming and chemical short-cuts in an unthinking and uncritical way. One of the other dangers is that there are so many self-appointed experts on hand to give advice, much of it at best misguided and at worst downright dangerous. Drugs and other short-cuts almost invariably lead you into trouble. The best way to get where you want to go is the natural way. It may take

Correcting a client's exercise technique in a one-to-one coaching session.

longer, but when you get there you will know that you have earned it. You did it honestly and you will not have to worry about any hidden risks to your health.

BODYBUILDING FOR THE OVER-THIRTY-FIVES

Eddie Ferrie

Bodybuilding is a curious phenomenon and my own relationship to it has always been a love–hate one. I loved exercising and the feelings of strength and vitality that came from training hard with weights, and the way it was possible to transform the body. The things I hated were being told what I could and could not eat, and the fact that the sport was riddled with anabolic steroids and people who pretended that they did not take them! I had been very overweight but basically strong and healthy from the age of eight until I was about nineteen when I got into serious training as a member of the British National Judo Squad and sorted out my weight problem, albeit only for about ten years!

My reasons for writing this book with Dennis Oakes stem from having had a serious weight problem, something that affects millions of people, both men and women, in modern life. In the modern world we tend to

First-time contest win for Eduardo Merino Postigo, who is also a powerlifting champion.

Eddie Ferrie, aged 38, 287lb (130kg), before ...

... and after, aged 39, 220lb (100kg) – what a difference a year makes!

think and act in straight lines. My background is in martial arts, judo in particular, where one of the underlying principles is that of circularity, of circles within circles, which encourages us to take a more holistic view of things. The relationship between cause and effect is not always as straightforward as it appears.

In my twenties I found controlling my weight simple, if not easy. I did judo five or six times a week, ran from two to five miles every day and did weight training three times a week on average. I was pretty well addicted to exercise, but the results were extremely positive, so it was hard to know at the time that most of the time I was overtraining.

I competed at national and international levels at super-heavyweight, weighing in at 287lb (130kg), at light-heavyweight 190–210lb (86–95kg) and at heavy middleweight 172–190lb (78–86kg). The lightest I have been since the age of twelve was 185lb (84kg), when I competed at heavy middleweight in 1983.

All good things come to an end, however, and work, marriage and family commitments increasingly cut into the time I had available for training. I stopped competing seriously in 1986, weighing about 210lb (95kg), and put on an average of about 11 or 12lb (5 or 6kg) a year over the following six years and almost without realizing it, ended up weighing 310lb (140kg).

As part of my conditioning programme, I had always done a lot of roadwork and spent a lot of time in gymnasiums doing strength and fitness circuits with weights. For me, running was always an essential part of controlling my weight. Unfortunately, however, the combination of being very overweight as a child and later doing lots of sport was a damaging one. In my early thirties, I began to develop a hip problem. At first I noticed a slight limp, but no pain, and being permanently busy with other things, I did not pay it much attention. The hip slowly got worse and I began to notice my mobility decrease as the joint gradually stiffened up. Eventually, when it became painful, I had the problem diagnosed medically. It turned out to be osteoarthritis.

Children who are overweight often damage their hip joints without very much in the way of symptoms being manifest, so normally the damage does not become apparent until the early fifties when arthritic symptoms crop up. When overweight children later do a lot of sports, they accelerate the joint degeneration. Judo was not the ideal sport for someone with already damaged hips, but I enjoyed it enormously and I probably did more damage road-running, pounding out the miles on hard surfaces at quite a heavy body weight, than moving around on the mat.

Arthritis is a painful and depressing condition and it was these two factors more than any others that made it vital for me to lose weight and get back into reasonable condition. In my mid-thirties I had lost and regained weight yo-yo fashion by making dietary adjustments, but since I was no longer able to practise judo – the sport I loved – I had found other forms of training unsatisfying. Everything felt wrong because of the way my hips worked – and too time consuming to be practical. I inevitably regained weight. For about five years, I hovered around the 275lb (125kg) mark. It was only when the arthritis became really debilitating and walking became a real difficulty that I realized that it had degenerated from being a nuisance into a painful, misery-producing health problem that needed priority attention. One of the big dangers with a gradually degenerating condition is that we adapt to it and evolve all sorts of coping strategies to help us to put up with the way things become, instead of trying to change them. It is so easy to rationalize why you do or do not do things, and so easy to rationalize incorrectly. The dysfunction becomes normal and it becomes hard to remember things ever having been different.

This worsening condition coincided with a decision to go and live in Spain for family reasons, which allowed me to begin to reorganize my life, working less and giving more priority to taking care of myself through exercise. I have been living in Spain for three years and have been training with Dennis Oakes who I met here. Training together, we have been able to develop a formula based on a combination of common sense, inspiration, enthusiasm, mutual support and persistence that has worked to get me back into reasonable physical condition and let him make important improvements in his fitness and physique too.

Where I learned an enormous amount was in the areas of diet and recuperation. I also relearned certain things, things I had forgotten. The most important was the role the mind plays in shaping and controlling the

Checking shoulder and back posing.

body. Inspiration is essential, and we all have to find it wherever we can. My personal physical transformation has been remarkable. It took some time to get the right formula, working around difficulties caused by the arthritis and other factors, but in the last year, training with Dennis and following specially worked-out diets, I was able to lose 55lb (25kg) of blubber and gain about 7 to 9lb (3 to 4kg) of muscle, in spite of not being able to run. I have maintained my new bodyweight at 220lb (100kg). In the process, I also avoided the immediate necessity of a double hip-replacement operation, arrested the deterioration of my joints and recovered some functionality in my damaged hips.

Bodybuilding for me is not a linear process. Holidays, binges, work commitments and so on inevitably have a negative effect. One of the key points is not to let small 'failures' assume an exaggerated importance. You may go astray with your diet, pick up a niggling injury, or have a lay off occasionally – all factors that would sabotage preparation for a contest, but which really are not that important if you simply want to keep in good shape. So long as you remember what your goals are and keep making the small, daily efforts at readjustment, cutting out refined sugars, fats and salt. And keeping going back to training. In spite of the interruptions you will generally stay on course without any sense of sacrifice or self-denial. The process itself is very rewarding and allows for a continuous redefining of goals and a sense of ongoing progress.

The back and shoulders of Dennis Oakes.

I am continuing to make progress and will continue to do so. This year my target is to slowly lose another 20lb (10kg) so as to return to a lean, stable bodyweight of 200lb (90kg). For the over-thirty-fives, the real contest is to have a happy, healthy life. Natural bodybuilding and everything it teaches us about diet, exercise and recuperation is one way to win that contest.

Index